HOME
AND
FAMILY LIFE
EDUCATION

55 Projects, Games, and Activities

Mary Holbrook
and
Shirley Van Horne

J. Weston Walch, Publisher
Portland, Maine

Users' Guide
to
Walch Reproducible Books

As part of our general effort to provide educational materials which are as practical and economical as possible, we have designated this publication a "reproducible book." The designation means that purchase of the book includes purchase of the right to limited reproduction of all pages on which this symbol appears:

Here is the basic Walch policy: We grant to individual purchasers of this book the right to make sufficient copies of reproducible pages for use by all students of a single teacher. This permission is limited to a single teacher, and does not apply to entire schools or school systems, so institutions purchasing the book should pass the permission on to a single teacher. Copying of the book or its parts for resale is prohibited.

Any questions regarding this policy or requests to purchase further reproduction rights should be addressed to:

Permissions Editor
J. Weston Walch, Publisher
P.O. Box 658
Portland, ME 04104-0658

—J. Weston Walch, Publisher

2   3   4   5   6   7   8   9   10

ISBN 0-8251-1794-1

Copyright © 1991
J. Weston Walch, Publisher
P.O. Box 658 • Portland, Maine 04104-0658

Printed in the United States of America

Contents

UNIT II. FOOD AND NUTRITION ACTIVITIES

UNIT III. HOUSING ACTIVITIES

UNIT IV. CONSUMER EDUCATION ACTIVITIES

UNIT V. RELATIONSHIPS ACTIVITIES

UNIT VI. CLOTHING ACTIVITIES

UNIT VII. CHILD DEVELOPMENT ACTIVITIES

Introduction

Home and Family Life education continues to alter and expand in an effort to meet the needs of our society. Middle-level students need to be helped to understand that all of us—male and female, young people and adults—are involved in consumer and homemaking roles. There is also a definite need for students to learn and practice the skills of cooperation and problem solving.

Home and Familiy Life Education provides up-to-date activities relating to major issues affecting teens and their families. The activities are all appropriate for both boys and girls in a coeducational setting at the sixth- to ninth-grade level.

Cooperative teams are used for many of the activities. Almost all of the projects could be used with individual students as well as in groups.

Also important, *Home and Family Life Education* is designed to provide creative and fun activities for students and teachers.

Teaching Guide
and Answer Key

Unit I.

Classroom Management Activities

Educational Objectives

Students will become better acquainted with their classmates and develop a level of trust which will help provide a positive classroom climate.

Students will evaluate and suggest topics to be studied in class, and therefore, build a sense of ownership.

Introduction

Classroom management at the middle level requires a great deal of organization and ingenuity. The activities included in this section are designed to assist you with the following:

1. Introducing students to one another and developing a positive climate for discussion and cooperative group work.

2. Encouraging students to read and evaluate up-to-date information that relates to topics covered in Home and Family Life Classes.

3. Providing recognition for individual students and groups of students as they participate in class projects.

4. Evaluating the social skills of students.

It is our belief that these activities will help students to develop a sense of belonging and cooperation and, thus, a positive classroom climate.

Your Ideas Are Important

Educational Objectives

Students will evaluate topics and suggested teaching methods to provide input for you.

Hints for Preparation and Uses

1. This activity provides you with information about the topics and teaching methods that are most interesting to a particular class. Students enjoy the opportunity to provide input for their teachers. This survey could also be used with parents, either individually at parent conferences or in a group situation, such as Open House.

2. Since "Your Ideas Are Important" includes topics that span all of the broad areas covered in Home and Family Life curricula, this survey will work best when used at the beginning of a course that includes a variety of topics.

3. Early in the course, you should explain to your students that their ideas and needs are important and will be considered as learning experiences are planned. Give the students the option of completing the survey anonymously. You could tally survey results and share them with the class so that students can see the topics and teaching methods that are most popular with their class.

4. Since it is important that Home and Family Life courses adapt to the needs and focus of the families in the community, "Your Ideas Are Important" could also provide valuable input from parents and community members. This will assure you of parent and community support for the Home and Family Life program.

Find the Match

Educational Objectives

Students will become acquainted with each other and develop a positive classroom environment conducive to cooperative learning.

Hints for Preparation and Use

1. "Find the Match" is an active "get-acquainted activity" which encourages students to meet and talk with many of the other students in the class. Too often, teachers overlook the need for students to learn the names of their classmates and develop rapport with one another. This activity fosters both of those needs.

2. After distributing "Find the Match" to each student, you should read and explain the rules to the class. Encourage the students to learn their classmates' names as they acquire autographs. Inform the students that they will have 15 minutes to complete the activity.

Possible Follow-up Activities

1. To identify areas of similarity among classmates, you could read each question and ask students who could "autograph" that question to raise their hands.

2. Randomly call on students and ask them to read off the names and identify each of the students who autographed their paper. You could award prizes or special recognition to those students who were able to identify all of the students who had autographed their paper.

This Is Me!

Educational Objectives

Students will identify and share with the class members their primary interests and personal favorites.

Students will develop rapport with each other as they learn more about each other.

Hints for Preparation and Use

1. "This Is Me!" is a creative project that encourages students to identify and share information about themselves with their classmates. A positive classroom environment develops as the students learn more about each other and begin to feel comfortable.

2. Materials needed:
   "This Is Me!" handout
   blank paper
   colored marking pens and/or crayons
   magazines
   scissors

3. After distributing a copy of "This Is Me!" and a piece of blank paper to each student, explain that the students may trace the face provided on the handout or draw a picture of themselves. They can use words and pictures cut from magazines or create their own to list their personal favorites.

Follow-up Activities

1. After the pictures are completed, ask each student to select three of the items on their picture to share orally with the class. Each student then shows his or her picture to the class and shares the three personal favorites they have selected.

2. Display the pictures on a bulletin board so students can look at all of them. Tell students the pictures will be posted for one week so the students can "study" them. After the pictures have been taken down, as a quiz for extra credit, have each student write the names of all the other students in class and two of the favorites each had given. You could award a special recognition certificate to those students with perfect scores.

3. When you display the pictures in the classroom, cluster together the pictures of students who sit together.

4. Use "Teamwork" as a follow-up activity. See below.

Teamwork

Educational Objectives

Students will identify and share with class members their primary interests and personal favorites.

Students will develop rapport with each other as they learn more about each other.

Students will practice the skills needed for working together in cooperative teams.

Hints for Preparation and Use

1. "Teamwork" is designed to be used as a follow-up activity after "This Is Me!" After students complete "This Is Me!" individually, you place them in teams and ask them to compare their collages looking for areas of agreement. Lively discussions develop as the students attempt to settle on their team's "Most Favorites" and "Least Favorites." This activity is very effective in introducing students to group work and helping group members to get to know one another and feel comfortable working together.

2. You can assign students randomly (numbering off or drawing from a fishbowl, for example) or you could select teams before introducing the assignment. It is best NOT to allow the students to select their teams. Groups of two, three, or four are most effective. Individual participation decreases if the group is larger.

3. Before introducing this assignment, go over the following expectations for group work:

   a. Location of groups in the classroom and seating arrangements: Suggest that the students should be sitting "knee to knee, eye to eye."

   b. Staying in group: Students are to remain in their group during the entire activity, ignoring those in other groups.

   c. Noise control: Students are to speak in quiet voices which can only be heard by their group.

   d. Listening skills: One person talking, eye contact, taking turns, asking questions for clarification.

   e. Group consensus: When group members disagree, consensus can only be reached through discussion and compromise. All group members have equal votes.

4. You may wish to have small groups of students briefly demonstrate how these skills look when used correctly.

5. Distribute one copy of "Teamwork" to each cooperative team. Explain that team members will need to discuss their ideas until they all agree. No answer should be written down until all group members have agreed to it. After the assignment has been completed, team members should review their answers until everyone in the group knows them all.

6. While the groups are working, you circulate and monitor how well the students are working together and using the skills reviewed. After group work is completed, focus on those teams that were successfully using the skills, citing specific examples.

7. Collect the completed "Teamwork" assignments and randomly select one student from each group. Ask that student to recite specific answers the team wrote down.

   Example: What is your team's favorite movie?
   What is your team very good at?

May I Present My Friend . . .

Educational Objectives

Students will develop rapport in the classroom as they become acquainted with each other.

Students will practice speaking to a group.

Hints for Preparation and Use

1. "May I Present My Friend . . ." pairs students up to find out more about each other. Each student then introduces her or his new-found friend to the class.

2. Assign students in pairs using a random method such as numbering off or selecting names from a fishbowl. If the class has an uneven number of students, you can be a student's partner. Allow about 15 minutes for the students to interview each other. The students are to take turns interviewing each other and recording the answers so each one will be able to introduce his or her partner to the class. After the students have completed their interviews, they should ask additional questions until they can identify at least two things they have in common with their partner.

3. Before the students present their introductions, suggest to them that they look for similarities among class members.

4. Depending on time available for this activity, you may wish to have the students share all of the information about their partners, or you can tell them to select two or three facts to be shared.

Follow-up Activities

1. Discuss or have individual students write down some of the patterns they noticed. For example: There are a lot of middle children in this class.

2. Students can be asked to write down one thing they now know about each class member.

Magazine Reports

Educational Objectives

Students will analyze and evaluate information found in magazine articles related to topics studied in class.

Hints for Preparation and Use

1. Magazine articles provide some of the most current information related to Home and Family Life issues. This activity provides a systematic, interesting way to encourage students to read and share up-to-date information. Teachers who do not use a textbook may find this to be an especially helpful way to include some reading activities.

2. Magazine Reports included in this material encompass the following subject areas:

   Consumerism
   Food and Nutrition
   Housing and Home Furnishings
   Clothing Management
   Personal Relationships
   Child Development

3. You could assign the appropriate magazine report at the beginning of that unit within a comprehensive Home and Family Life course. As you introduce the assignment, you may want to have a variety of appropriate magazines available so the students will have a clear understanding of the type of magazine to use. You could point out some of the specific articles in the sample magazines. You could also provide the students with a list of the magazines available in the school library and in the Home and Family Life classroom.

4. You may wish to use this assignment or a variation of it as an option for students who have missed an assignment that can't be made up.

Follow-up Activity

Have the students briefly report in class on the article they read.

Evaluation

After the students have done oral presentations to the class, have each student make up three to five questions covering important points from their report. You can select questions to be used and compile them into a quiz for the class.

Behavior Bonus Game

Educational Objectives

Students will be able to understand the relationship between individual behavior and success in class.

Hints for Preparation and Use

1. The "Behavior Bonus Game" is an excellent tool for holding students accountable for inappropriate behavior and rewarding positive behavior. Students assist with scoring, so the system can be implemented with minimal disruption to class activities. This system is also very useful in providing concise information concerning student behavior for parent conferences.

2. Before introducing the "Behavior Bonus Game" to the students, you will need to decide on a specific number of points students will earn daily. These points may become part of the students' grade or be awarded as extra credit. You will then need to determine the point loss for each of the infractions. A sample list of point values is provided below.

3. After you complete the "Behavior Bonus Game" Point Sheet, you can distribute copies of it to your students so they know what behaviors will cost them how many points.

4. You will also need to record student names on a copy of the "Behavior Bonus Game" Record Sheet for each class (a different name on each numbered line; enough for 30 students on one sheet).

5. Each week a different student will be assigned to act as Game Keeper. You, not the Game Keeper, determine the infraction and tell the Game Keeper to record it on the "Behavior Bonus Game" Record Sheet.

Behavior Bonus Game

Infractions	Point Loss
1. Out of seat (during lecture, demonstration, etc.)	5
2. Talking after the bell has rung	5
3. Talking during demonstrations or lectures	5
4. Making silly noises, yelling	5
5. Unsafe practices	5
6. Horseplay	10
7. Fighting	15
8. Not raising hand	5

(continued)

Behavior Bonus Game (continued)

Infractions   Point Loss

Infraction	Point Loss
9. Interrupting	5
10. Cleanup not completed	10
11. Inappropriate language/swearing	10
12. Talking back	15
13. Disturbing/distracting others	5
14. Coming to class unprepared (no pencil, etc.)	5
15. Throwing things	10
16. Unkind remarks toward classmates	15
17. Tardy to class	5
18. Other, as designated by teacher	

Participation Certificates

Educational Objectives

Students will be recognized individually or as teams for class achievements.

Hints for Preparation and Use

1. Students at the middle level enjoy individual and group recognition. They are very proud of certificates and awards presented to them. These certificates make each student feel special.

2. We have included three different award certificates: Outstanding Achievement, Outstanding Performance, and Teamwork Award.

3. The Teamwork Award is an excellent tool for recognizing and focusing on students who are using the social skills needed for successfully working in cooperative teams. We feel it is a good idea to recognize and reward those students who are modeling the behavior we would like to see in all of the students.

Rate This Class

Educational Objectives

Students will provide feedback to you to facilitate improvement.

Hints for Preparation and Use

1. "Rate This Class" has been included as an evaluation tool to be used toward the end of the course. Information provided by the students is very helpful to you in planning for future classes.

2. Encourage students to provide answers that reflect careful thought. Since they are not required to put a name on this evaluation, students should feel comfortable providing honest answers. In order to maintain anonymity, you may wish to provide a large envelope for collecting the student evaluations.

Unit II.

Food and Nutrition Activities

Educational Objectives

Students will be able to interpret and evaluate information found on food labels.
Students will be able to identify foods in the Basic Four food groups.
Students will be able to use cookbooks and define cooking terms found in recipes.

It's on the Label

"It's on the Label" is designed to teach students to make use of specific information found on food labels. General information required by law is included as well as nutritional labeling.

Hints for Preparation and Use

1. Collect food labels from a variety of packaged foods. These can be frozen, canned, or dehydrated. Examples of foods include combination rice or pasta dishes, frozen entrees, cereals, and dessert mixes. Avoid single foods, such as frozen corn. This assignment is most effective if a different label is available for each student, but you could also use the assignment with cooperative learning teams. You can mount the food labels on poster board and/or laminate them to make them easier for the students to work with.

2. Before assigning "It's on the Label," you will need to review the following terminology with your students:
   brand name
   generic name
   ingredients—always listed from largest to smallest amount
   pull date
   UPC (Universal Product Code)
   nutritional labeling
   U.S. RDA (United States Recommended Daily Allowance)

Follow-up Activities

1. You could ask each student or cooperative learning team to show the class their label and share one or two important facts contained on it.

2. Have students compare the nutritional information contained on three to five different labels for similar products and select the food that is the best nutritional choice.

3. After information about each label has been orally presented to the class, have each student write down the three foods he or she would be most likely to want to purchase and the three foods she or he would be least likely to purchase, with reasons for the choices.

Evaluation

Have the students list and explain five items a food label is required by law to provide.

Basic Four Game

This lively, competitive game helps reinforce information about the foods contained in each of the Basic Four food groups. The students complete this activity while working in cooperative learning teams. The "Basic Four Game" is designed to follow a lesson on the foods contained in the Basic Four food groups and the application of the Basic Four to nutritional planning.

Hints for Preparation and Use

1. To prepare for the "Basic Four Game," you will need to make five copies of the worksheet for each cooperative learning team. You may wish to have small prizes available for the teams who win the competition.

2. Distribute one copy of the "Basic Four Game" sheet, turned face down, to each cooperative learning team and explain that, at the signal, they are to circle all of the foods on the sheet that belong in the meat/protein group. Foods should be circled if any portion of the food belongs to this group.

3. As soon as a team feels they have correctly circled all the foods in that group, they take their paper to you. Using the answer key on pages 14–18, you check the answers but do not write on the paper. You tell the team how close they are to all the correct answers. Example: "You missed two foods and have circled one food incorrectly." The teams continue working until one of the teams has all correct answers.

4. You then distribute another copy of the "Basic Four Game" sheet to each cooperative learning team and instruct the teams, at the signal, to circle foods contained in the fruits and vegetables group. Competition continues until one team has all the correct answers.

5. This process is repeated for the milk group, the breads and cereals group and the fifth group; fats, oils, and sugars.

Evaluation

Have each student classify the following list of foods into the appropriate food group(s):

rice	spaghetti with meatballs
eggs	Canadian bacon pizza
peanut butter sandwich	strawberry milkshake

Meat/Protein Group Key

milk	(tacos)	applesauce
oatmeal	(deviled egg)	bagels
strawberries	fruit yogurt	corn chips
cinnamon roll	blueberry muffin	root beer
orange juice	fruit punch	noodles
(French toast)	German chocolate cake	(cheeseburger (with roll))
cantaloupe	(cheese pizza)	(smoked salmon)
croissants	(roast turkey)	(barbecued spareribs)
chocolate milk	corn on the cob	cherry Jell-O
(scrambled eggs)	mashed potatoes	chocolate pudding
(eggnog)	cranberry juice	potato salad
tomato juice	pasta salad	(salami)
watermelon	French fries	ripe olives
grapefruit	popcorn balls	(peanut butter)
(walnuts)	chocolate candy bar	(cottage cheese)
toast and jelly	cola	(liver)
whole wheat bread	peaches	baked apple
grape juice	strawberry shortcake	grits
(baked beans)	lemon-lime soda	chocolate ice cream
coffee (if sugared)	vanilla milkshake	banana split
(pork chops)	raspberries	hot buttered biscuit
(omelet)	shredded wheat with bananas	bran flakes
(bacon)	(spaghetti and meatballs)	soy sauce
ketchup	baked potato	iced tea (if sugared)

Milk Group Key

milk

oatmeal

strawberries

cinnamon roll

orange juice

French toast

cantaloupe

croissants

chocolate milk

scrambled eggs

eggnog

tomato juice

watermelon

grapefruit

walnuts

toast and jelly

whole wheat bread

grape juice

baked beans

coffee (if sugared)

pork chops

omelet

bacon

ketchup

tacos

deviled egg

fruit yogurt

blueberry muffin

fruit punch

German chocolate cake

cheese pizza

roast turkey

corn on the cob

mashed potatoes

cranberry juice

pasta salad

French fries

popcorn balls

chocolate candy bar

cola

peaches

strawberry shortcake

lemon-lime soda

vanilla milkshake

raspberries

shredded wheat with bananas

spaghetti and meatballs

baked potato

applesauce

bagels

corn chips

root beer

noodles

cheeseburger (with roll)

smoked salmon

barbecued spareribs

cherry Jell-O

chocolate pudding

potato salad

salami

ripe olives

peanut butter

cottage cheese

liver

baked apple

grits

chocolate ice cream

banana split

hot buttered biscuit

bran flakes

soy sauce

iced tea (if sugared)

Fruits and Vegetables Group Key

milk	(tacos)	(applesauce)
oatmeal	deviled egg	bagels
(strawberries)	(fruit yogurt)	corn chips
cinnamon roll	(blueberry muffin)	root beer
(orange juice)	(fruit punch)	noodles
French toast	German chocolate cake	cheeseburger (with roll)
(cantaloupe)	cheese pizza	smoked salmon
croissants	roast turkey	barbecued spareribs
chocolate milk	(corn on the cob)	cherry Jell-O
scrambled eggs	(mashed potatoes)	chocolate pudding
eggnog	(cranberry juice)	(potato salad)
(tomato juice)	pasta salad	salami
(watermelon)	(French fries)	ripe olives
(grapefruit)	popcorn balls	peanut butter
walnuts	chocolate candy bar	cottage cheese
toast and jelly	cola	liver
whole wheat bread	(peaches)	(baked apple)
(grape juice)	(strawberry shortcake)	grits
baked beans	lemon-lime soda	chocolate ice cream
coffee (if sugared)	vanilla milkshake	(banana split)
pork chops	(raspberries)	hot buttered biscuit
omelet	(shredded wheat with bananas)	bran flakes
bacon	spaghetti and meatballs	soy sauce
ketchup	(baked potato)	iced tea (if sugared)

Breads Group Key

milk	(tacos)	applesauce
(oatmeal)	deviled egg	(bagels)
strawberries	fruit yogurt	(corn chips)
(cinnamon roll)	(blueberry muffin)	root beer
orange juice	fruit punch	(noodles)
(French toast)	(German chocolate cake)	(cheeseburger (with roll))
cantaloupe	(cheese pizza)	smoked salmon
(croissants)	roast turkey	barbecued spareribs
chocolate milk	(corn on the cob)	cherry Jell-O
scrambled eggs	(mashed potatoes)	chocolate pudding
eggnog	cranberry juice	(potato salad)
tomato juice	(pasta salad)	salami
watermelon	(French fries)	ripe olives
grapefruit	(popcorn balls)	peanut butter
walnuts	chocolate candy bar	cottage cheese
(toast and jelly)	cola	liver
(whole wheat bread)	peaches	baked apple
grape juice	(strawberry shortcake)	(grits)
(baked beans)	lemon-lime soda	chocolate ice cream
coffee (if sugared)	vanilla milkshake	banana split
pork chops	raspberries	(hot buttered biscuit)
omelet	(shredded wheat with bananas)	(bran flakes)
bacon	(spaghetti and meatballs)	soy sauce
ketchup	(baked potato)	iced tea (if sugared)

Fats, Oils, and Sugars Key

milk

oatmeal

strawberries

cinnamon roll

orange juice

French toast

cantaloupe

croissants

chocolate milk

scrambled eggs

eggnog

tomato juice

watermelon

grapefruit

walnuts

toast and jelly

whole wheat bread

grape juice

baked beans

coffee (if sugared)

pork chops

omelet

bacon

ketchup

tacos

deviled egg

fruit yogurt

blueberry muffin

fruit punch

German chocolate cake

cheese pizza

roast turkey

corn on the cob

mashed potatoes

cranberry juice

pasta salad

French fries

popcorn balls

chocolate candy bar

cola

peaches

strawberry shortcake

lemon-lime soda

vanilla milkshake

raspberries

shredded wheat with bananas

spaghetti and meatballs

baked potato

applesauce

bagels

corn chips

root beer

noodles

cheeseburger (with roll)

smoked salmon

barbecued spareribs

cherry Jell-O

chocolate pudding

potato salad

salami

ripe olives

peanut butter

cottage cheese

liver

baked apple

grits

chocolate ice cream

banana split

hot buttered biscuit

bran flakes

soy sauce

iced tea (if sugared)

It's Snackin' Time

As students analyze the nutrients contained in their favorite snack and compare their favorite snack with those of other class members, they become aware of what they should consider when selecting snacks.

Hints for Preparation and Use

1. You will need to have available old magazines, scissors, and glue for the students to use to locate pictures and mount them to "It's Snackin' Time." You will also have to have books with nutritional information for individual foods available. This information is frequently found in appendixes of food and nutrition textbooks. Another source is *The Nutritive Value of Foods*, available from the USDA by contacting the Cooperative Extension Service.

2. Begin this lesson by having the students brainstorm a list of snacks. After compiling a list, ask the students to evaluate which foods on the list have the best nutritional value.

3. Have the students complete "It's Snackin' Time" working individually.

4. After completing the assignment, the students can work in groups to make a poster featuring all of the group's "It's Snackin' Time" worksheets. These are shared with the class, and a list is compiled as each of the groups presents its snacks.

5. After all of the snacks chosen by the class members have been presented, lead the students in evaluating the snacks and identifying the nonnutritional ones.

Evaluation and Follow-up Activities

1. The students could make a list of suggested snacks for each of the Basic Four food groups.

2. Have students write an evaluation of the snack they analyzed for "It's Snackin' Time."

Nutrition Bingo

"Nutrition Bingo" provides an excellent way to review nutrition information and definitions while holding student interest.

Hints for Preparation and Use

1. Before having the students play "Nutrition Bingo," you will need to cover the terms listed on the worksheet, using the definitions provided on the bingo call cards.

2. You will need to provide a "Nutrition Bingo" worksheet for each student, plus markers. Colored squares cut from construction paper make good markers.

3. To play the game: .

   a. Distribute "Nutrition Bingo" to each student and instruct the class to select words from the list provided, writing one word in each blank space.

   b. Distribute markers to use in playing the game.

   c. You or a student reads one of the nutrition definitions.

   d. Students place a marker over the word they believe is the right answer, if that word is on their card.

   e. When a student has covered five spaces across, down, or diagonally, she or he calls out "Nutrition!" and says the answers as they are checked by the caller. The winning student may be allowed to "call" the next game.

4. The competition increases if you have small food prizes available for those students who win.

Is It Safe to Cook?

This is a quick and easy activity which enables students to understand the importance of safety as it relates to cooking. This activity should be used before cooking labs with middle-level students.

Hints for Preparation and Use

1. To introduce this activity, you may wish to ask students to share descriptions of kitchen accidents they know about.

2. The students should complete "Is It Safe to Cook?" individually, listing ten safety rules and the reason for following each rule.

3. After each student has completed his or her list, the students should work with the others in their cooking lab group and make a list of the ten best rules provided by their group.

Evaluation

Tell students: Select your cooking lab's ten most important rules. Working together, create a poster listing those ten rules which will be posted in your kitchen.

What's for Dinner?

"What's for Dinner?" introduces students to a variety of food preparation methods and encourages them to read recipes and explore cookbooks.

Hints for Preparation and Use

1. You will need to cover the following food preparation terms and their definitions:

   Bake: Cook by dry heat in an oven.

   Barbeque: Roast on coals or an open fire; cook meat in a highly flavored sauce.

   Boil: Cook in liquid in which bubbles rise continuously to and break on the surface.

   Braise: Brown and then cook, covered, in a small amount of liquid over low heat until tender.

   Broil: Cook over or under direct heat.

   Deep fat fry: Cook in a deep container in enough hot oil to cover the food.

   Fry: Cook, uncovered, in a small or moderate amount of fat or oil.

   Microwave: Cook in a microwave oven.

   Pan-broil: Cook, uncovered, on a hot surface, pouring off fat as it accumulates.

   Poach: Cook in a simmering liquid in a covered pan.

   Roast: Cook meat or poultry in the oven by dry heat.

   Sauté: Cook in a small amount of fat, keeping the food in motion.

   Simmer: Cook in liquid just below the boiling point.

   Steam: Cook over boiling water in a perforated container.

   Stir-fry: Cook in the Oriental method, cutting food into small pieces and cooking it briefly, while stirring, in hot oil.

2. You will need to make a copy of the list of individual foods provided and cut the slips apart so the students can draw a food from a container, such as a fishbowl. You will also need to have a variety of cookbooks available for student use.

3. Working in pairs, the students are to locate recipes that contain their assigned food. Each recipe located is to represent a different food preparation method.

Evaluation

Have each group briefly name the food they were assigned and share at least four different preparation methods they were able to find.

Countdown to Dinner

"Countdown to Dinner" introduces middle-level students to time management in food preparation, as well as to organizing food supplies and equipment. It is a very useful introductory activity prior to lab activities that involve preparing several different parts of a meal.

Hints for Preparation and Use

1. You will need to have a variety of cookbooks available for the students to use in completing this activity.

2. Use the overhead masters included here to make transparencies. Using the Sample Menu transparency, discuss the order of preparation that would be most effective for achieving the goal of having all of the foods ready to serve at the same time. Using the Main Dish overhead transparency, demonstrate for the students the process of listing the utensils, equipment, and food needed.

3. After completing this process for the sample menu and main dish using the overhead projector, have each student select a menu and complete the time work plan and a list of food, supplies, and utensils needed for their main dish.

Evaluation

Discuss with the students which staple food supplies and equipment are most important in their home. Do different families rely on different food staples and equipment for their food preparation? If so, why?

Unit III.

Housing Activities

Educational Objectives

Students will be able to describe major factors that influence people's housing choices.
Students will be able to explain home safety and security practices.
Students will be able to analyze different values and needs relating to housing.
Students will be able to investigate resources and services available in their immediate community.

In My Opinion, a Home Should . . .

"In My Opinion, a Home Should . . ." encourages students to think about what is important to them in relation to housing. It also provides an opportunity to compare their housing values and opinions with those of other students in the class.

Hints for Preparation and Use

1. This activity is designed to be used as an introductory activity for the unit on housing. The "In My Opinion, a Home Should . . ." statements can be grouped into the following categories:

   Home safety and security: 9, 10, 17, 19, 21, 25
   Home atmosphere: 5, 6, 7, 8, 12, 13, 14, 26, 27, 30
   Neighborhood and community: 1, 3, 16, 20, 24, 28
   Housing selection: 2, 4, 11, 15, 18, 22, 23, 29

   Note: The numbers following each category above refer to the numbers on the "In My Opinion, a Home Should . . ." statements.

2. These statements can be distributed to cooperative learning teams in a variety of ways.

   a. Focus on one of the categories each day and begin the lesson by assigning a different statement to each cooperative learning team. After discussion, the cooperative learning team shares its best answer with the rest of the class.

   b. Assign all of the statements for one category to a cooperative learning team and have team members share the answers they arrived at with the rest of the class.

   c. Have each student select, from a fishbowl, one of the "In My Opinion, a Home Should . . ." statements and share his or her own reaction with the rest of the class.

3. Since there are a total of 30 "In My Opinion, a Home Should . . ." statements, you may wish to assign one statement to each of the students to answer individually. Even if you do choose this strategy, you may wish to have only five or six students share their answers on one day, so the students can concentrate on the shared opinions and compare them with their own values.

4. You will need to make copies of the "In My Opinion, a Home Should . . ." statements and cut them into strips to be distributed to teams or students.

Evaluation

Ask the students, "What picture comes to mind when you think about the 'perfect' home? Are there differences among your answer and those of your classmates?" Conclusion: No two people have the same ideas about the "perfect" home.

The Inside Story of My Home

Whether students live in an apartment or a house, it is helpful for them to be aware of the information covered in "The Inside Story of My Home." Many middle-level students are beginning to experience being home alone for longer periods of time.

Hints for Preparation and Use

1. Encourage students to complete this activity with the help of their parents. This is helpful because it encourages communication about the material being covered in the course and because students need to be aware of the correct answers for their house or apartment.

2. Two versions of "The Inside Story of My Home" are provided so students can investigate for their personal living situation.

3. You could introduce this activity with some problem situations for the students to suggest solutions. For example:

   a. If you found a leak under your kitchen sink, what should you do?

   b. If the hot water stopped working, what should you do?

4. Allow students adequate time to work with their parents to complete this activity—at least over a weekend.

Evaluation

Divide the class into groups, and give each group a problem to tell the class how to solve. Examples could include:

1. If the lights went out in the kitchen, what could you do to fix them?

2. How do you turn the water off?

3. Where are different places the circuit-breaker boxes can be located?

4. Where is it recommended that fire extinguishers be located?

Safe, Not Sorry

Since many middle-level students are in latchkey situations, there is a definite need for students to learn about personal safety practices. As the students are discussing these issues in cooperative learning teams and with the rest of the class, they may discover that many of their classmates have concerns similar to theirs. Encourage students to discuss these questions with other family members.

Hints for Preparation and Use

1. Have the students discuss the questions on "Safe, Not Sorry" in their cooperative learning teams. They should then complete the assignment using the answers their entire group feels are best. You may wish to ask different groups to share their answers to a particular question with the rest of the class. Discussion of the reasons for their answers may follow.

2. As a follow-up activity, you may wish to invite a local police officer to speak to the class on home security and safety.

Evaluation

Answers to "Safe, Not Sorry" will provide a means of evaluation.

Fire Safety Savvy

"Fire Safety Savvy" is designed to be used in conjunction with "The Inside Story of My Home" and "Safe, Not Sorry." We believe that middle-level students need to study all of these topics in order to feel more competent as they begin to spend more time home alone or to take on baby-sitting commitments.

Hints for Preparation and Use

1. This activity could be completed in cooperative learning teams or individually. You could assign it as an in-class project or to be completed at home after discussion with parents.

2. Many local fire departments have speakers who are available to talk to schools about home fire safety. This could be a follow-up activity to this assignment.

Evaluation

Have the students write out their answer to the following question:

"It's 2:00 A.M. and the smoke detector wakes you up. What will you do?" Include a step-by-step sequence of the necessary actions to take.

Focus on Safety

"Focus on Safety" is designed to be used as an introductory activity to stimulate student thinking and creativity on the topic of household security and safety.

Hints for Preparation and Use

1. Instruct cooperative learning teams to brainstorm a list of rules for home safety and security. *After* they can show you a list of at least ten rules, ask them to complete the "Focus on Safety" worksheet.

2. "Focus on Safety" can also be used as a competitive game with small prizes available to the cooperative learning team that completes it first. If you are going to use it as a game, it is important that you have all of the teams begin working at the same time.

Evaluation

Have each student select one safety rule and explain the importance of following it.

Living Space Case Studies

"Living Space Case Studies" is designed to help students understand how housing can and should be selected to provide for specific needs of individuals and families. Using a problem-solving approach, the students apply information about the various types of housing alternatives to the case study they are assigned.

Hints for Preparation and Use

1. You will need to discuss the advantages and disadvantages of various types of housing. For example:

SINGLE-FAMILY HOME

Advantages: more privacy, yard, you own it, can remodel, increases in value

Disadvantages: expensive, requires more land, higher heating bills.

APARTMENTS

Advantages: monthly expenses are stable, less upkeep, major repairs done by owner, can move on short notice

Disadvantages: less privacy, may be noisy, more restrictions, no control over rent increases, cannot remodel

DUPLEX/MULTIPLEX

Advantages: uses less land, convenient and flexible, may be easier for families with children or pets, could own or rent

Disadvantages: May be expensive, fewer recreation facilities than an apartment, close neighbors, rules about remodeling

CONDOMINIUMS

Advantages: may offer special facilities, less upkeep, you own the unit, increases in value, may paint or remodel

Disadvantages: since purchased, not rented, may be more difficult to move; less privacy; may be noisy; monthly fee for grounds upkeep; rules

MOBILE HOMES

Advantages: less expensive and more privacy than apartment, may come with furniture and appliances, less upkeep, could be moved, you own it

Disadvantages: Difficult to move, may be restricted as to site, less safe, value depreciates quickly, may not meet fire codes

2. Since newspaper ads are required for this activity, you will need to collect several newspapers or ask students to bring the classified ads from their home newspapers to use for this assignment.

3. You will need to cut the "Living Space Case Studies" apart and place them in a container such as a fishbowl. Enough case studies have been provided so that each student could work on a case study individually, or you could select some of the case studies and have the students work in cooperative learning teams.

4. Have each student or cooperative learning team share their case study and their housing choices orally with the class. This provides additional insight on the relationship among needs, values, and housing choices.

Evaluation

Have the students briefly describe the type of housing they plan to choose when they first live on their own and the reasons for their choice.

This Is My Community

"This Is My Community" is designed to help students become better acquainted with the services and businesses available in their community.

Hints for Preparation and Use

1. To introduce this activity, it would be helpful if you could make a transparency of the neighborhood area surrounding your school and perhaps the closest business section of the community. Remove the street names and numbers from the map before you make the transparency. Using the transparency map, have the students identify the streets and other important landmarks on the map.

2. You may also want to survey the class to determine how many of the students have lived in this community for more than five years. Less than one year? All their life? If they are willing, have the students who have recently moved to the community share some of the first feelings they had as they moved into the community.

3. This activity works very well with cooperative learning teams. It is very helpful to have a phone book or city directory available to each of the cooperative learning teams.

4. Students should give an address and approximate directions from their school to the destination.

5. As a follow-up activity, students could visit, or call five of the businesses or agencies listed on "This Is My Community" and write a brief summary and evaluation of the services provided.

Evaluation

Have the students work individually, or in groups, to compile a list of places they would need to locate if they had just moved into a new community. They should explain the order in which these places should be contacted and be able to explain why that order is important.

Design a Community of the Future

"Design a Community of the Future" is a creative, engaging project which teaches the interrelationships of community services and the planning that has taken place to assure that the needs of community members are met.

Hints for Preparation and Use

1. Prior to introducing this project, cover the following:

   a. Brainstorm some of the specific characteristics and needs within the community students are living in today. For example: government offices, parks and recreation facilities, service agencies, stores, residential areas, transportation.

   b. Have the class discuss possible characteristics and needs of their community 25 years from now. What major changes might take place?

   c. What are the similarities and differences between today's community and their vision of the community of the future?

2. This activity is designed to be done by cooperative learning teams. You will need to provide materials such as graph paper, construction paper, rulers, and marking pens so the students can show the community layout.

3. Allow the students two to four days to complete the assignment. It will be helpful to assist the students in developing a time line for work to be completed each day.

4. As the students present their community plans to the class, you should utilize opportunities for discussions about how people's needs and wants are met by communities and the types of changes we might anticipate in the future.

Evaluation

As a class, brainstorm the common aspects of all of the communities designed in class. Describe what communities are like now and compare that with the communities described in this activity.

Unit IV.

Consumer Education Activities

Educational Objectives

Students will be able to understand how to manage a checking account.
Students will be able to make a spending plan based on income and expenses.
Students will be able to make acceptable consumer choices based on wants and needs.
Students will be able to define the terminology of consumerism.

Managing a Checking Account

This project enables students to practice the skills involved in maintaining a checking account. Encourage students to communicate with their families as they learn about the use of checking accounts.

Hints for Preparation and Use

1. Lead a discussion about the advantages and disadvantages of personal checking accounts. Some possible answers include:

   Advantages
   a. You don't have to carry cash.
   b. You have a record of money transactions.
   c. You don't have to use money orders.
   d. It's convenient.

   Disadvantages
   a. Some places won't cash checks.
   b. Checking accounts require careful record-keeping.
   c. You need to have proper identification to cash checks.
   d. Most checking accounts cost money.

2. Photocopy the blank checks and deposit slip *twice* for each student. Give each student two blank checks from the handout. Go over the correct procedure for writing a check. Have each student write out the check to any person for any amount. Walk around the room and monitor each student's work.

3. Have the students write the second check for $44.21. Assuming they had a balance of $162.93 before writing the second check, ask what their balance is after the check is written. (Answer = $118.72.) Continue monitoring work as students complete their computations.

4. Distribute one of the following case-study assignments to each of the students:
   Sally Shortskirts
   Bruno Broadbottom
   Sam Saddlesoap
   Laura Lostlove
   Also distribute the other handouts with the blank checks and deposit slip.

5. Explain to the students that there are four different case studies and that each student is expected to complete his or her own work independently. They are allowed to use scratch paper in calculating their answers. NOTE: Decide whether to allow the use of calculators for this assignment.

6. When all students have completed the assignment, place students in cooperative learning teams with other students who have been working on the same case study. Have the students compare answers and decide on one set of correct answers which they will turn in for their team.

Answers

SALLY SHORTSKIRTS

Balances:
$689.12 savings
$184.08 checking (beginning)
$ 61.72 checking (ending)

Deposits:
$15.00 checking

Checks to be written:			
Bridle Trails Horse Barn	$62.84	check fee	$ .15
Seventeen	$18.00	" "	$ .15
Bon Marché	$23.42	" "	$ .15
Nordstrom's	$32.50	" "	$ .15

BRUNO BROADBOTTOM

Balances:
$18.64 savings
$72.27 checking (beginning)
$24.57 checking (ending)

Deposits:
$22.50 checking

Checks to be written:			
Magnificent Music Store	$22.75	check fee	$0
Burgerville	$ 2.09	" "	$0
Nordstrom's	$18.84	" "	$0
Payless	$26.52	" "	$0

SAM SADDLESOAP

Balances:
$1,668.52 savings
$ 0.00 checking (beginning)
$ 109.05 checking (ending)

Deposits:
$200.00 checking

Checks to be written:			
Science Fiction Book of the Month Club	$12.58	check fee	$ .20
Modern Music Store	$27.65	" "	$ .20
K Mart	$31.90	" "	$ .20
Payless	$18.02	" "	$ .20

LAURA LOSTLOVE

Balances:
$197.42 savings
$ 84.22 checking (beginning)
$ 55.26 checking (ending)

Deposits:
$13.50 checking

Checks to be written:			
Paul's Drug Store	$ 8.22	check fee	$ .10
Fashionable Fabrics	$ 9.62	" "	$ .10
JC Penney	$11.71	" "	$ .10
Johnny's Market	$12.51	" "	$ .10

Evaluation

Use the two following activities, "Leroy Taylor's Checking Account" and "Leroy Taylor's Vacation," as further practice and evaluation of these skills.

Leroy Taylor's Checking Account

This project provides additional practice in using a checking account. Middle-school students often need to practice this skill several times as you monitor their progress.

Hints for Preparation and Use

1. Have the students work on this assignment individually. You may wish to call this a practice test and follow the same rules that would apply in a testing situation; this will prevent students from sharing answers.

2. Use the answer key below to go over the correct answers with the students so they can review the correct procedure, if necessary.

Answers

Number	Date	Check	Amt. of Check		Fee	Deposit		Balance	
								1,846	.83
1010		Rainier View Apts.	460	.00	.20			1,386	.63
1011		Texaco	60	.47	.20			1,325	.96
1012		U.S. West Comm.	29	.83	.20			1,295	.93
1013		FoMoCo	314	.16	.20			981	.57
		deposit	.			802	.99	1,784	.56
1014		Dr. Toothaker	182	.42	.20			1,601	.94
1015		Puget Power	204	.99	.20			1,396	.75
		deposit				21	.47	1,418	.22
1016		United Airlines	99	.00	.20			1,319	.02
1017		The Bon Marché	142	.87	.20			1,175	.95
1018		Nordstrom's	63	.97	.20			1,111	.78
1019		U.S. Bank	400	.00	.20			711	.58

Evaluation

The activity provides a means of evaluation.

Leroy Taylor's Vacation

As the students work to calculate Leroy Taylor's bank balance, they will soon find out whether Leroy Taylor can afford to go on his vacation.

Hints for Preparation and Use

1. This activity has been designed to be used as a test at the end of the checking account unit.

2. Grading for this activity could be done in one of the following ways:

   a. The activity is considered Pass (A) or Fail. Students who are within $.10 of the correct answer for the final bank balance receive an A. If not, they fail. Students may retake the test until they achieve a Pass grade.

   b. Assign points for various stages throughout the assignment. Make the test worth _____ points based on the number of checkpoints assigned. For example:
   Checkpoints could be at check numbers 1023, 1026, 1029, and 1032, and at the end of the calculations.

Answers

Number	Date	Check	Amt. of Check		Fee	Deposit		Balance	
								1,567	.95
1021		Rainier View Apts.	460	.00	.20			1,107	.75
1022		Puget Power	175	.86	.20			931	.69
1023		Chevron U.S.	162	.90	.20			768	.59
1024		Safeway	60	.00	.20			708	.39
		deposit				182	.42	890	.81
1025		Albertson's	45	.00	.20			845	.61
1026		Gene Juarez Hair Salon	18	.50	.20			826	.91
1027		JC Penney	68	.83	.20			757	.88
1028		Nordstrom's	142	.35	.20			615	.33
		deposit				651	.19	1,266	.52
1029		Dr. Anne Ginzberg	42	.50	.20			1,223	.82
1030		Place Two	192	.41	.20			1,031	.21
1031		American Express	188	.11	.20			842	.90
1032		Frederick & Nelson	104	.50	.20			738	.20
1033		Safeway	85	.00	.20			653	.00
		service fee	5	.00				648	.00

Shopping Spree

Students are allotted an imaginary amount of money to spend on their shopping sprees. This activity is a fun way to look at the effects of impulse buying.

Hints for Preparation and Use

1. Explain the rules of the game:
    a. Each student may purchase as many items as she or he wishes, as long as the student does not spend more than $350 on the first spree and $500 on the second spree.
    b. Once an item has been "purchased," the decision cannot be reversed.
    c. Students are to keep track of their purchases on the "Shopping Spree" record form.

2. Ask the students to imagine that they are on a shopping trip and have $350 ($500 for the second spree) to spend on anything they wish to buy.

3. Using the first set of "cards" provided (pages 127–165), show each item that can be purchased, one at a time. When you show an item, students decide if they want to purchase it.

4. After you have shown all of the first set of cards, discuss briefly how the students felt about their individual purchases. Were there any purchases they would change? Did any of them run out of money and want to purchase items that were offered later?

5. Have the students play the game again using the second set of cards (pages 167–205) and another blank "Shopping Spree" record form.

6. Ask students to compare the results of the two shopping sprees. Discuss impulse buying compared with planned purchases. Questions for discussion:
    Can you remember a time when you purchased something on impulse?
    How do stores cater to impulse buyers?
    What items do store managers place near checkout counters to encourage impulse buying?

Evaluation

Have students write a short essay on "How I Intend to Avoid Impulse Buying in the Future."

Discuss: "When is impulse buying OK?"

Consumerism from A to Z

Using dictionaries, textbooks, and other available resources, students work in teams to develop an alphabet of terms related to consumerism. This is a very effective way to review and increase vocabulary.

Hints for Preparation and Use

1. You will need to have some dictionaries and resource materials on consumer issues available for the students.

2. "Consumerism from *A* to *Z*" can be used in several different ways:

   a. To use as a competitive game:

      i. Divide the class into two groups.

      ii. Each team is to work cooperatively to develop an alphabet of consumerism, finding a word or phrase to go with as many of the letters of the alphabet as possible. For example:

      > *A* is for *advertising*.
      > *B* is for *budget* or *bank*.
      > *C* is for *consumer* or *checking account*.

      iii. Allow about 15 to 20 minutes for the teams to complete their alphabets.

      iv. Suggest to the teams that they have two answers in case there is a tie.

      v. Have the teams alternately share their alphabet words with the class. As the teams share their words, you or a student can write the words on a piece of butcher paper or on the chalkboard. Use a different-color pen or chalk for each team.

      vi. If one team cannot provide an alphabet word and the other team can, award 2 points. Allow 5 seconds for a team to answer.

      vii. If neither team can provide an alphabet word, skip that letter.

      viii. If the game is tied after completing the alphabet, go through it a second time for additional words.

   b. To make Alphabet Books:

      i. The students can work individually or in cooperative learning teams to create Consumerism Alphabet Books.

      ii. Encourage the students to use a variety of resources and visual mediums to create a finished product.

      iii. The students may wish to select a theme related to consumerism to use throughout their book—for example, Advice to Consumers or Consumer Resources.

      iv. This assignment can also be used as an extra-credit activity.

Where Does Family Income Go?

This activity was developed after parents requested that teachers help students understand how family income is spent. It is an enlightening activity for students and also encourages students to discuss money issues with their family.

Hints for Preparation and Use

1. Before using this activity, you will need to define and discuss the following terms as they relate to money management:
   Needs: Things that are essential.
   Wants: Things you desire to make life more satisfying.
   Fixed Expenses: Expenses that are the same on a regular basis.
   Flexible Expenses: Expenses that can be adjusted by you, usually related to wants, rather than needs.

2. You may also want to have the class brainstorm a list of fixed and flexible expenses that are typical for most families.

3. Assign the students to cooperative learning teams. Give each team the first page of "Where Does Family Income Go?" Do not distribute page two at this time. Each team is to invent a family, including a family name and brief descriptions of the family members; then the team identifies the family's needs and wants. To help the students understand this part of the assignment, you may wish to go over a brief example with the class. We suggest that you make up an example that reflects some of the typical characteristics of families in your school's community.

4. Three income levels may be used: Gross yearly incomes of $18,000, $24,000, or $30,000. This should be determined by the income levels of your school's community. Provide the teams with the gross monthly income they are to assume their family earns. For page two, provide the Social Security and federal income tax figures.

Gross Yearly Income	Gross Monthly Income	Federal Withholding	Social Security
$18,000	$1,500	$ 85.00	$112.65
$24,000	$2,000	$163.00	$150.20
$30,000	$2,500	$235.00	$187.75

5. Each cooperative learning team is to list the specific items they think the family's monthly income will be spent on, the amount spent, and whether each item is a want or a need.

6. At this point, you may wish to select randomly a few cooperative learning teams and have them share their family information with the class. You could do this by making an overhead transparency of the "Where Does Family Income Go?—Phase One" worksheet and filling in the information as it is shared by the cooperative learning team.

7. Distribute page two of "Where Does Family Income Go?" to the cooperative learning teams. Ask them to revise the distribution of income so their figures match those of the average family. You will want to provide calculators for this portion of the assignment so the students can calculate the percentages for each budget category.

8. Discuss the differences in the figures between page one and page two, and how the various cooperative learning teams would adjust their page one amounts to be more in line with the page two figures.

9. If desired, the cooperative learning teams could make a poster to show their family's needs and wants and their choices for distribution of family income.

Evaluation

Have each student list typical fixed and flexible expenses for a family with teenagers.

Unit V.

Relationships Activities

Educational Objectives

Students will understand that happiness and success depend on how a person relates to others.
Students will be able to analyze relationships among family members.
Students will be able to analyze the relationship of values, goals, and one's self-concept.
Students will be able to describe teenagers' rights and responsibilities.

Safety First for Me

It is becoming increasingly important for young people to be made aware of personal safety practices. This activity is designed to cover a variety of personal safety situations and appropriate ways of handling them.

Hints for Preparation and Use

1. Introduce this activity by asking the students to suggest ways to deal with the following scenarios.

    WHAT IF:

    a. Somebody calls your house and asks, "Who is this?"

    b. Somebody tells you that your parents sent him or her to pick you up because your parents have been in an accident.

    c. A family member was to pick you up at 7:00. It is 7:30, and she or he still hasn't arrived.

    d. You are in a theater and someone suspicious sits down behind you, then follows you to the rest room or snack bar.

2. Have the students complete "Safety First for Me" in cooperative learning teams so they can share ideas. Tell them to choose their team's best personal safety tip to share with the rest of the class.

3. Ask each student to take home the "Safety First for Me" worksheet and discuss it with their parents. Extra credit could be given to those students who do that and have their parents or caregiver sign the worksheet.

Evaluation

Have each cooperative learning team create a collage or poster depicting personal safety to be displayed in the school.

What Do You Value?

The ever-popular T-shirt is used to illustrate each student's personal values. This is a creative way of introducing an important topic for the middle level.

Hints for Preparation and Use

1. You will need to have the following items available for this activity:
   tag board T-shirt pattern
   glue
   butcher paper or construction paper
   scissors
   magazines for cutout pictures

2. Hold up a $1.00 bill and a personal family picture. Ask the students, "Do each of these have value? Which would you choose?" Explain that values are individual to each person. Values are personal!

3. Have each student complete the "What Do You Value?" assignment sheet.
   Sample Responses:
   #1. Define personal values:
       Beliefs, objects, or ideas that a person considers to be important.
   #2. Where does a person get his or her own values?
       Family, friends, media, school, church, books.
   #3. Why do one person's values differ from the values of his or her closest friends?
       Each person has had a different set of experiences that have influenced his or her beliefs.
   #4. What are some values that meet with society's approval? See list in #5 on the worksheet.

4. Distribute butcher paper or large pieces of construction paper to each student. Have them make a T-shirt out of their paper.

5. Each student is to use magazine pictures or drawings to represent her or his five most important values. Words cannot be used.

6. Tell the students to leave their names off their T-shirt.

7. Display the T-shirts around the room.

8. Have the students try to guess the owner of each of the T-shirts.

Evaluation

Discuss how personal values influence everyday decisions.

Family Want Ads

As students write want ads describing the perfect parent, teenager, and brother or sister, and for themselves, they begin to recognize more fully the value of focusing on positive characteristics of family members. This may lead to an appreciation of the contributions of other family members.

Hints for Preparation and Use

1. Ask the students to imagine that they are selling a stereo tape player and radio. If they were writing a classified ad to sell the stereo, what types of words would they need to use? Whenever you are selling something, you purposely do not focus on the negative characteristics of that item. It becomes necessary to focus on the positive characteristics.

2. Tell students that this assignment asks them to focus on positive qualities they would like to see in other family members, and then to write want ads to sell the perfect parent, perfect teenager, and perfect brother or sister, and to sell themselves.

3. Have students share their want ads with other members of their cooperative learning team. Each team then shares their best ad with the rest of the class.

Evaluation

As a class, design one want ad for each category. Write these out on a big poster to be displayed on a bulletin board.

Family Portrait

Each student draws a portrait of the family they plan to have as they envision it in 25 years. As students share their pictures with the class, they begin to understand that their personal visions of their future families can be unique.

Hints for Preparation and Use

1. Materials needed: marking pens, colored pencils or crayons, "Family Portrait" handout.

2. Ask the students, "How do you picture yourself in 25 years? How old are you? What will you look like? Where will you live? Are you married or single? Who is in your family?"

3. Have each student draw a "Family Portrait" to represent the family he or she expects to have in 25 years. Tell the students that their artistic ability is not important. We are concerned with their vision of their future family.

4. Have each student show the family portrait to the rest of the class and explain her or his reasons for choosing this family.

Evaluation

Have students write a paragraph or discuss in their cooperative learning team "What is a family?"

Mapping Out the Rest of My Life

This activity is designed to make students think about the major events in their life so far and those they anticipate occurring in the future. Specific goals and plans may affect a student's map. After the life maps are completed, students may discuss how teenage parenthood, substance abuse, dropping out of school, or other teen crisis situations would change their life map.

Hints for Preparation and Use

1. You will need to prepare a long piece of butcher paper with selected headings from "Mapping Out the Rest of My Life." For example, you could include the following (ages listed in parentheses are possible ages that these events might occur):

Your own birth   _____

Your first job (age 16)   _____

Your first boyfriend/girlfriend (age 16)   _____

Moving out on your own (age 18)   _____

Your first car (age 20)   _____

Getting married (age 22)   _____

Birth of first child (age 24)   _____

Birth of last child (age 27)   _____

Last child leaves home (age 49)   _____

Retirement (age 65)   _____

Own death (age 79)   _____

2. Give each student a copy of "Mapping Out the Rest of My Life." Explain to the students that we all are aware that we can't totally control when each of these events will occur, but this activity does give each person a chance to think about the specific goals they have for themselves.

3. After students have completed the "Mapping Out the Rest of My Life" assignment, have each student use felt marking pens to place their life map on the butcher paper.

4. You can lead a class discussion, which should include the following:
   a. "What would you consider the average age for each of these events?" After the students have suggested their answers, fill in the average age given for each item in number 1 above.
   b. What trends do you see when you look at all the entries on the butcher paper life map? For example:
      How many people chose to get married?
      At what age did most people list having their first child?
      Did anyone choose to remain single?
      How many chose to remain childless?

Evaluation

Have the students answer one or more of the following questions:

1. "What effect would becoming a teenage parent have on some of the things you want to do with your life?"

2. "How would your life map change if you were to win the lottery?"

3. "How would your life map change if you were to drop out of school at age 17?"

4. "How would your life map change if you moved at least 2,000 miles away?"

Teen Rights and Responsibilities

As students work to complete this activity, they begin to understand the interrelationship of responsibilities and rights. As teens successfully assume more responsibilities, they may acquire additional rights.

Hints for Preparation and Use

1. You may wish to send a brief letter home explaining that the students will be working on a project that focuses on teenage rights and responsibilities. Suggest that this could be a topic of discussion at home, with the discussion culminating in the "License for Teenagers" document (see next page).

2. This activity is designed to be done in cooperative learning teams. Have each group of students develop their list of teen rights and responsibilities.

3. After completing their list of teen rights and responsibilities, each cooperative learning team needs to reach consensus on the priority ranking of their list of teen rights and their list of teen responsibilities.

4. As a follow-up to this activity, discuss the importance of maturity, honesty, and open communication in maintaining a sense of trust within the family. Suggest to the students that they discuss the topic of teen rights and responsibilities with their parents or caregiver. (See "License for Teenagers" below.)

Evaluation

Have groups of students briefly debate the parents' and teens' point of view concerning teen rights and responsibilities.

License for Teenagers

Students use the "License for Teenagers" at home. Parents and teens identify the specific responsibilities and rights within their family.

Hints for Preparation and Use

1. This activity is designed to be used by the students with their parents. Encourage the students to keep the lines of communication open!

2. Students can use the list of teen rights and responsibilities, arranged by priority, to help guide their discussion with their parents or caregiver.

3. After students and parents/caregiver have agreed on the rights and responsibilities within their family, they can fill out, sign, and date the "License for Teenagers."

4. Students may wish to compare their completed licenses in class.

5. Have students discuss how their family conferences progressed. What difficulties did they encounter? What went smoothly? Was a real consensus reached?

Evaluation

Have students decide which license(s) they think is (are) most satisfactory.

Unit VI.

Clothing Activities

Educational Objectives

Students will be able to make wise clothing purchases.
Students will be able to explain how clothes affect our impressions of other people.
Students will be able to compare and evaluate various types of clothing stores.

Super Shopper

We have become a nation of clothing consumers rather than producers. "Super Shopper" helps students learn about the importance of careful selection of ready-to-wear clothing.

Hints for Preparation and Use

1. To introduce this lesson, ask the students if they have ever purchased an item of clothing that has become a disappointment because of quality.
   If so, what specific parts of the garment caused problems?

2. Distribute "Super Shopper" to each student. Assign the students to cooperative learning teams. Have each team discuss specific answers for each item on the worksheet.

3. After the students have completed "Super Shopper" in their cooperative learning teams, you could have the students share some of the answers they have by randomly calling on different groups to share their answers. These could be compiled on the chalkboard or on the overhead projector.

4. Suggested answers for "Super Shopper" are provided below.

Style:	Classic lines.
	Attractive colors and appearance.
Fabric:	Garment hangs smoothly and evenly.
	Plaids and stripes match at seams.
	Fabric used is appropriate for garment.
Care label:	Care directions are permanently attached.
	All parts of garment can be cared for in the same way.
	Care is appropriate for type of garment.
Seams:	Stitching is smooth and even, with short stitches.
	Seam edges are not raveling.
	Thread blends with fabric.

Hems:	Hem is even width all the way around garment.
	Hem is flat and smooth, is not noticeable.
Sleeves:	Smooth seams.
	Cuffs are even and attractively done.
Collar:	Even, lies flat, same on both sides.
Trim:	Neatly done, attractive and secure.
Zippers/	Neat, even stitching.
closures:	Opens, closes easily, tab locks.
	Fasteners are firmly attached.
	Fasteners are attractive on garment.
Buttons/	Buttonholes are sturdy, even.
buttonholes:	Buttons fit in buttonholes.
	Garment lies flat when buttons are buttoned.
Fit:	Allows room to reach, stretch, sit down, bend.
	Length looks good on you.

Evaluation

Have students bring an item of clothing to class and, in an oral presentation, describe the item in terms of the details listed on the "Super Shopper" worksheet.

Headless People

Your clothes reveal a great deal about you. Students are asked to describe people based on pictures without heads. It soon becomes apparent that we tend to place people into stereotyped roles based on their appearance and clothes.

Hints for Preparation and Use

1. Make overhead transparencies of the "Headless People" and separate transparencies of the corresponding heads.

2. Show the class the transparencies of the "Headless People." Ask the students to write a short biography of each person. These descriptions should include information about the person's occupation, age, lifestyle, and other items students feel are important.

3. After everyone is finished, randomly select some students to share their answers with the class.

4. Place the heads transparency on the "Headless People." Put the opposite heads on the bodies to see if people are tending to stereotype clothing with male or female faces.

5. Discuss differences between students' original biographies and their perception now that they see the matching heads.

Evaluation

Have students describe a person's clothes and let others guess the person's occupation. Discuss whether it is always possible to determine a person's occupation by by that person's clothes.

Where Can I Shop for Clothing?

Most people tend to think of shopping for clothing at one or two types of stores. However, a variety of stores sell clothing. This activity exposes students to the many types of clothing stores and the advantages and disadvantages of each.

Hints for Preparation and Use

1. This activity can be done in cooperative learning teams or individually. Another way to complete the activity would be to assign one type of store to each cooperative learning team. You could encourage teams to visit an example of their assigned store and present the information to the rest of the class. As each cooperative learning team reports to the class, the rest of the students could be filling in the answers on their assignment sheet.

2. Specific information about each type of store is included below.

THRIFT STORE

Definition:	A store that sells only used merchandise.
Advantages:	Clothing may be available for a very low price.
Disadvantages:	Clothing may be stained or very worn.
	Items cannot be returned. Current styles will not be available.

CONSIGNMENT SHOP (RESALE SHOP)

Definition:	A store that sells second-hand garments that are in very good condition; they often look new.
Advantages:	Clothing is available at prices lower than retail. More recent and classic styles are available.
Disadvantages:	Clothing cannot be returned.

FACTORY OUTLET

Definition:	A store with merchandise from a particular company sold in a warehouse setting.
Advantages:	Clothing is usually sold at reduced prices.
Disadvantages:	Clothing may be seconds or irregulars. Few services are available. Clothing cannot be returned.

CHAIN STORE

Definition:	A store found at more than one location, usually several, may be all over the state or even the nation.
Advantages:	Similar merchandise and quality at all locations; can be exchanged or returned at any of the store's locations.
Disadvantages:	Few styles to choose from; more likely to see someone else with the same clothing.

SPECIALTY SHOP

Definition:	A store that only sells one type of clothing, such as shoes or children's clothes.
Advantages:	May offer extra services and handle special orders; many items to choose from; handles one specific item.
Disadvantages:	Prices may be higher; locations may be less convenient.

DEPARTMENT STORE

Definition:	A store that is divided into many different sections with a variety of clothing.
Advantages:	Wide selection; a few extra services may be available; many sales.
Disadvantages:	May have higher prices; fewer choices in specific items.

DISCOUNT STORE

Definition:	A store that sells clothing and other items at lower prices than department stores.
Advantages:	Lower prices; many choices in common sizes.
Disadvantages:	Fewer services; may be lower quality.

SHOPPING MALL

Definition:	A mall area with many different department stores and specialty shops together.
Advantages:	Save travel time; great selection in one location.
Disadvantages:	Usually go there for a shopping expedition, not to run in for one specific item.

MAIL ORDER

Definition:	Merchandise is available by mail or phone order from catalogs.
Advantages:	Convenient; can shop from home.
Disadvantages:	Buying sight unseen; sizes may be more difficult to determine; colors may not be appropriate; have to wait for delivery; shipping and handling charges can add up.

"PARTY TIME"

Definition:	Merchandise is shown at someone's home by a hostess. Customers order merchandise to be delivered later.
Advantages:	Social time in someone's home.
Disadvantages:	More expensive; feel obligated to buy, have to wait for delivery.

Evaluation

Give students a list of clothing purchases they are to pretend they will be making. They are to list the type of store they would choose for each purchase and the reason why.

Your Clothing Costs

As students complete "Your Clothing Costs," they become more aware of the cost of their clothes and their family's total clothing costs. This activity also encourages discussions with parents about the actual dollars their family spends on clothing and other items.

Hints for Preparation and Use

1. Ask the students to estimate the cost of the clothing they are now wearing. This includes the cost of items such as contact lenses and eyeglasses. Students fill in the amounts on "Your Clothing Costs."

2. Survey the class to determine total dollars in their estimates:
   Less than $50
   $50 to $100
   Over $100
   Over $200

3. Ask each student to multiply his or her estimated costs by the total number of people in his or her family. Ask: "What does it cost to clothe your entire family?"

Evaluation

Have the students complete the Summary Questions on "Your Clothing Costs."

What Would I Wear When . . . ?

"What Would I Wear When . . . ?" helps students clarify the main principles of clothing selection and the importance of wearing an appropriate outfit for the occasion.

Hints for Preparation and Use

1. Supplies needed: Magazines that can be cut apart, glue, construction paper, marking pens.

2. Distribute the "What Would I Wear When . . . ?" assignment to each student or to cooperative learning teams. Each person or team is to select four of the situations on the lists and find magazine pictures to illustrate the type of clothing that should be worn for that occasion.

3. The pictures should be mounted on construction paper and displayed in the classroom.

Evaluation

Discuss with the students how they would feel if:

   a. You were wearing jeans and everyone else was dressed up?

   b. Your doctor was wearing a dirty shirt?

   c. You came to a new school and everyone was dressed totally differently than you were?

Unit VII.

Child Development Activities

Educational Objectives

Students will be able to use safe and appropriate techniques when caring for children. Students will be able to select and evaluate play activities suitable to a child's age and stage of development.

Baby-sitting Basics

"Baby-sitting Basics" is designed to be used as a pretest or introductory activity for a unit on baby-sitting and child care. Discussion of these issues provides further insight into the importance of safety and thinking ahead in successfully working as a baby-sitter.

Hints for Preparation and Use

1. Divide the students into cooperative learning teams. We recommend this format for this activity because we feel the discussions as the students complete the statements can provide important insights. Also, it is possible that some students will not have done any baby-sitting before and they will be able to benefit from the experience of others on their team.

2. You may choose to have each group complete all of the statements, or you could assign two or three statements to each cooperative learning team.

3. After the students have completed the activity, randomly call on cooperative learning team members to share their answers.

Evaluation

Discuss or have students write out answers to this statement:
   "Many important responsibilities are involved in baby-sitting."

Baby-sitting Dilemmas

The use of problem-solving skills is a very important part of baby-sitting and child care. "Baby-sitting Dilemmas" places students in the position of deciding how to handle a difficult baby-sitting situation in the most appropriate way.

Hints for Preparation and Use

Photocopy the "Baby-sitting Dilemmas" situations and cut them apart. Place them in a container such as a fishbowl. Have each student draw one of the baby-sitting dilemmas from the container. Proceed in one of the following ways.

a. Have each student read his or her baby-sitting dilemma to the class and give a solution immediately. This method illustrates for the students the necessity of a quick response when problems arise.

b. Have each student draw a different baby-sitting dilemma. Assign the students to cooperative learning teams of three or four students. Have each student share his or her baby-sitting dilemma and a solution with the students on the team. Additional suggestions can be shared within the group and the best solution written down to be turned in.

c. Have the students write out on the worksheet their options and their recommended solution to the baby-sitting dilemma they drew from the fishbowl. This method emphasizes the importance of considering all of your options before taking action.

Evaluation

Give the students a short quiz using several of the baby-sitting dilemmas as potential baby-sitting problems for the student to solve.

Design a Child

"Design a Child" is a creative activity that introduces the topics of parental expectations for children and individual differences among people.

Hints for Preparation and Use

1. Give each student the blank picture of a "child."

2. Ask students to describe the following about their child. They can write this information on the back of the sheet or on the sides around the picture:
   a. Is it a boy or a girl?
   b. When will he/she take the first steps?
   c. What will be his/her favorite nursery rhyme?
   d. After growing up, what will be her/his career?

    e. What is her/his favorite food? least favorite food?

    f. What will be his/her best subject in school? worst subject?

    g. What will be her/his highest ambition in life?

    h. What is the name of your child?

3. After answering these questions, the students use crayons or markers to "design" their child.

4. Completed "children" make an appealing classroom display. Often students will bring other students into the room to show them their "child." As the students are sharing information about the child they designed, you have an opportunity to discuss how important it is to allow children to be themselves—not someone "designed" by another person.

Evaluation

Discuss how everyone started out as two cells and how different we each are from one another. Relate that to this assignment: Everyone's child started out exactly the same; now look how different they are from one another.

As Children Grow, They Change

This activity helps the students understand and appreciate stages of development and specific characteristics at each age level.

Hints for Preparation and Use

1. You will need to have resource materials such as books and magazine articles available for the students to look up information.

2. Divide the students into seven cooperative learning teams. Each team will be assigned or will select one of the age groups to find information about. Team members need to work together to locate and fill in all of the information on the assignment sheet. The students may need up to a full class period to complete their research.

3. Have the cooperative learning teams create a poster or some other visual aid to present the information they acquired. Students could be copying down the information from each report on additional copies of "As Children Grow, They Change."

Evaluation

Give the students a list of skills and behaviors that are typical of children at various stages. Have the students categorize them according to the age at which they occur.

Children's Work Is Play

"Children's Work Is Play" offers students a choice and some guidelines as they create a toy, story, or game for a preschooler. This activity serves as an excellent medium for applying the information acquired about preschool-age children from the activity "As Children Grow, They Change."

Hints for Preparation and Use

1. Introduce the assignment by explaining that students are to create a toy, game, or story for a preschool-age child. This assignment will provide a finished product that could be used with preschoolers when the student is baby-sitting for or playing with them.

2. After going over the three options and the guidelines for these projects, you should:

   a. Brainstorm games, stories, and toys the students remember as particularly enjoyable when they were preschool-age.

   b. Show the class some samples of all three choices and discuss what characteristics make these particularly appealing to that age group.

3. Provide materials and some class time to work on this project, but the students should understand that they will probably have to finish the project on their own time.

4. You may choose to contact a local preschool or day-care center to see if your middle-level students could use their project with the preschool's or center's children. This could become a community service project for your students and also give them exposure to preschool children.

Evaluation

Evaluate projects according to the guidelines listed on the "Children's Work Is Play" handout.

Reproducible Pages

UNIT I
Classroom Management Activities

Your Ideas Are Important

If you would like to have some input on what will happen in class this term, take a few minutes to fill these two sheets out to help your teacher determine course content. You do not need to put your name on these sheets.

	Extremely Interested	Very Interested	Somewhat Interested	No Way!
Alcohol/drug abuse in teens	_____	_____	_____	_____
Child abuse	_____	_____	_____	_____
Community services	_____	_____	_____	_____
Eating disorders	_____	_____	_____	_____
Fitness and nutrition	_____	_____	_____	_____
Self-esteem	_____	_____	_____	_____
Independent living skills	_____	_____	_____	_____
Careers/job skills	_____	_____	_____	_____
Consumer decisions	_____	_____	_____	_____
Leadership skills	_____	_____	_____	_____
Selecting housing	_____	_____	_____	_____
Furnishing a home	_____	_____	_____	_____
Selecting clothing for self	_____	_____	_____	_____
Clothing care	_____	_____	_____	_____
Teen crises	_____	_____	_____	_____
Working with children	_____	_____	_____	_____
Preparing nutritious meals	_____	_____	_____	_____
Home and personal safety	_____	_____	_____	_____

(continued)

Your Ideas Are Important *(continued)*

Below are listed some teaching methods. Again, rank them by your own interest in seeing this method used in class.

	Extremely Interested	Very Interested	Somewhat Interested	No Way!
Lecture by the teacher	_____	_____	_____	_____
Class discussions	_____	_____	_____	_____
Outside speakers	_____	_____	_____	_____
Field trips	_____	_____	_____	_____
Films, filmstrips, videos	_____	_____	_____	_____
Class members teach all or part of the lesson	_____	_____	_____	_____
Group assignments/projects	_____	_____	_____	_____
Individual assignments/projects	_____	_____	_____	_____
Taking quizzes/tests	_____	_____	_____	_____
Outside readings	_____	_____	_____	_____
Doing worksheets, then discussing them	_____	_____	_____	_____

Below is some space for you to tell your teacher what you would like to do in this class. Include things in school you enjoy as well as school things you do not particularly like to do.

_____

_____

_____

_____

_____

Find the Match

Rules:

1. You may get up and walk around.

2. When you find someone who can answer yes to a question on your paper, ask for his or her autograph.

3. One person can sign the same paper only twice.

Questions:

1. Were you born in another country?_____

2. Have you lived in another state? _____

3. Do you have both a brother and a sister? _____

4. Do you get to prepare at least one meal a week for your family?

   _____

5. Do you have a part-time job? _____

6. Do you speak another language at home? _____

7. Do you have a steady boyfriend/girlfriend? _____

8. Are you an only child? _____

9. Have you traveled out of state in the past year? _____

10. Do you have a pet? _____

11. Do you always eat breakfast before you come to school?_____

12. Have you made an article of clothing you like to wear?_____

13. Are you shy? _____

14. Have you helped to redecorate your bedroom?_____

15. Do you receive a weekly allowance from your parents?_____

This Is Me!

Directions: Each person has his or her own skills, interests and preferences. Let's find out about the uniqueness of each person in our class. On a blank piece of paper, draw a picture of yourself or trace the face below. Use words and pictures created by you or cut from a magazine to answer the items below. Write your name under your picture.

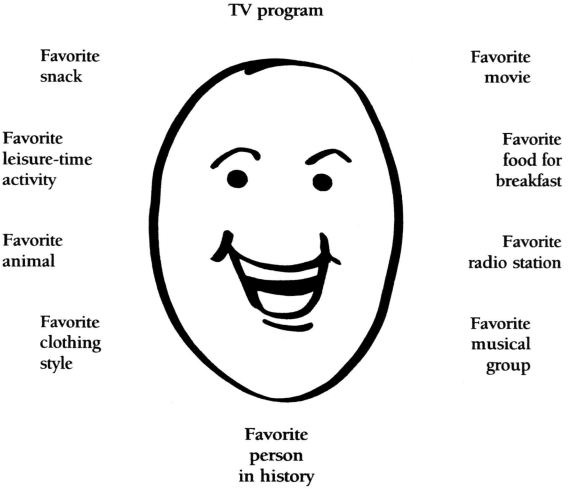

Favorite
TV program

Favorite
snack

Favorite
movie

Favorite
leisure-time
activity

Favorite
food for
breakfast

Favorite
animal

Favorite
radio station

Favorite
clothing
style

Favorite
musical
group

Favorite
person
in history

My name: _____

Home and Family Life Education

Teamwork

Team members: _____   _____

_____   _____

Select a team name: _____

Team Information:

Our team is very good at: _____

Our team wishes that: _____

Our team gets excited about: _____

Share ideas about the following with your group and decide on some answers that you can all agree about:

	Most Favorite	**Least Favorite**
Movie		
Music group		
Snack		
Animal		
Television show		
Clothing style		
Radio station		
Family activity		

Name _____ Date _____

May I Present My Friend . . .

Find someone in our class that you don't know or barely know and interview her or him. Fill in the information from your classmate in the blanks below. Then introduce your friend to the class.

1. My friend's full name is _____ .

2. She or he is in the _____ grade.

3. Some of the other schools she or he has attended are _____
   _____

4. She or he was born on _____ (date) in _____
   _____ (place).

5. During the past year, an exciting event in her or his life has been _____
   _____
   _____

6. He or she has the following hobbies and special interests: _____
   _____
   _____

7. Her or his school and after-school activities include _____
   _____
   _____

8. His or her favorite subject in school is _____ .

9. His or her favorite color is _____ .

10. What are her or his reasons for taking this class? _____
    _____
    _____

Home and Family Life Education

Consumerism Magazine Reports

Topics and Due Dates:

#1 _____ How to make a personal/family budget
Tips for caring for a home

#2 _____ Accident prevention in the home
Theft prevention in the home

#3 _____ Personal safety
A career related to family financial management

Guidelines for These Reports:

1. These reports must be in ink.

2. In order to get full credit, you must follow the correct form.

3. When completed, turn in the reports in your class file folder on the teacher's desk.

4. You may turn in the reports as they are due, or you may turn in all three for extra credit on the first due date.

5. You may use any current magazine for these reports—any library will have acceptable magazines, and there are some in class you may use before or after school.

6. Magazine reports are considered **home** work and are not to be done in class unless time is allowed for this.

Food and Nutrition Magazine Reports

Topics and Due Dates:

#1 _____ Ways to save time and energy in meal preparation
Tips for coping with rising food costs

#2 _____ Human nutrition
Weight control

#3 _____ Suggestions for planning or remodeling a kitchen
A career related to foods and food preparation

Guidelines for These Reports:

1. These reports must be in ink.

2. In order to get full credit, you must follow the correct form.

3. When completed, turn in the reports in your class file folder on the teacher's desk.

4. You may turn in the reports as they are due, or you may turn in all three for extra credit on the first due date.

5. You may use any current magazine for these reports—any library will have acceptable magazines, and there are some in class you may use before or after school.

6. Magazine reports are considered **home** work and are not to be done in class unless time is allowed for this.

Housing and Home Furnishings
Magazine Reports

Topics and Due Dates:

#1 _____ Current fashion trends
Tips on improving sewing skills

#2 _____ Ideas for selecting clothing
Caring for clothing

#3 _____ Saving money in wardrobe planning
A career related to clothing

Guidelines for These Reports:

1. These reports must be in ink.

2. In order to get full credit, you must follow the correct form.

3. When completed, turn in the reports in your class file folder on the teacher's desk.

4. You may turn in the reports as they are due, or you may turn in all three for extra credit on the first due date.

5. You may use any current magazine for these reports—any library will have acceptable magazines, and there are some in class you may use before or after school.

6. Magazine reports are considered **home** work and are not to be done in class unless time is allowed for this.

Name _____

Clothing Management
Magazine Reports

Topics and Due Dates:

#1 _____ Ideas for selecting home furnishings
Ideas for saving money

#2 _____ Suggestions for remodeling a home
Recent trends in home furnishings

#3 _____ Ideas for selecting family housing
A career related to housing or home furnishings

Guidelines for These Reports:

1. These reports must be in ink.

2. In order to get full credit, you must follow the correct form.

3. When completed, turn in the reports in your class file folder on the teacher's desk.

4. You may turn in the reports as they are due, or you may turn in all three for extra credit on the first due date.

5. You may use any current magazine for these reports—any library will have acceptable magazines, and there are some in class you may use before or after school.

6. Magazine reports are considered **home** work and are not to be done in class unless time is allowed for this.

Name _____

Personal Relationships Magazine Reports

Topics and Due Dates:

#1 _____ Solving personal and/or family problems
Teen crisis

#2 _____ Drugs and their effects on people
Methods of self-improvement

#3 _____ Solving family health problems
A career related to family and personal
relationships

Guidelines for These Reports:

1. These reports must be in ink.

2. In order to get full credit, you must follow the correct form.

3. When completed, turn in the reports in your class file folder on the teacher's desk.

4. You may turn in the reports as they are due, or you may turn in all three for extra credit on the first due date.

5. You may use any current magazine for these reports—any library will have acceptable magazines, and there are some in class you may use before or after school.

6. Magazine reports are considered **home** work and are not to be done in class unless time is allowed for this.

Child Development Magazine Reports

Topics and Due Dates:

#1 _____ Becoming a parent
Prenatal care

#2 _____ Information about birth defects
Needs of young children

#3 _____ Problems of growing up
A career related to children

Guidelines for These Reports:

1. These reports must be in ink.

2. In order to get full credit, you must follow the correct form.

3. When completed, turn in the reports in your class file folder on the teacher's desk.

4. You may turn in the reports as they are due, or you may turn in all three for extra credit on the first due date.

5. You may use any current magazine for these reports—any library will have acceptable magazines, and there are some in class you may use before or after school.

6. Magazine reports are considered **home** work and are not to be done in class unless time is allowed for this.

Name _____ Date _____

Magazine Report Form

Topic chosen _____

Report # _____

Title of article _____

Source _____

Date of issue _____

What was the purpose of this article? _____

_____

Summarize the article: _____

_____

_____

_____

_____

_____

_____

_____

_____

_____

_____

_____

What is your opinion of the article? _____

_____

_____

_____

Behavior Bonus Game Point Sheet

Infractions	*Point Loss*
1. Out of seat (during lecture, demonstration, etc.)	_____
2. Talking after the bell has rung	_____
3. Talking during demonstrations or lectures	_____
4. Making silly noises, yelling	_____
5. Unsafe practices	_____
6. Horseplay	_____
7. Fighting	_____
8. Not raising hand	_____
9. Interrupting	_____
10. Cleanup not completed	_____
11. Inappropriate language/swearing	_____
12. Talking back	_____
13. Disturbing/distracting others	_____
14. Coming to class unprepared (no pencil, etc.)	_____
15. Throwing things	_____
16. Unkind remarks toward classmates	_____
17. Tardy to class	_____
18. Other, as designated by teacher	
_____	_____
_____	_____
_____	_____
_____	_____

Home and Family Life Education

Behavior Bonus Game Record Sheet

						call home	out	conf
1.								
2.								
3.								
4.								
5.								
6.								
7.								
8.								
9.								
10.								
11.								
12.								
13.								
14.								
15.								
16.								
17.								
18.								
19.								
20.								
21.								
22.								
23.								
24.								
25.								
26.								
27.								
28.								
29.								
30.								

Game Keeper _____ Date _____

Rules:

1) Mark off points as indicated by the teacher.
2) Mark only in ink.
3) Return to vertical file after class.
4) All marks are final.
5) Turn in this sheet to teacher on Friday.

All marks were fairly and honestly recorded.

Signed _____

Home and Family Life Education

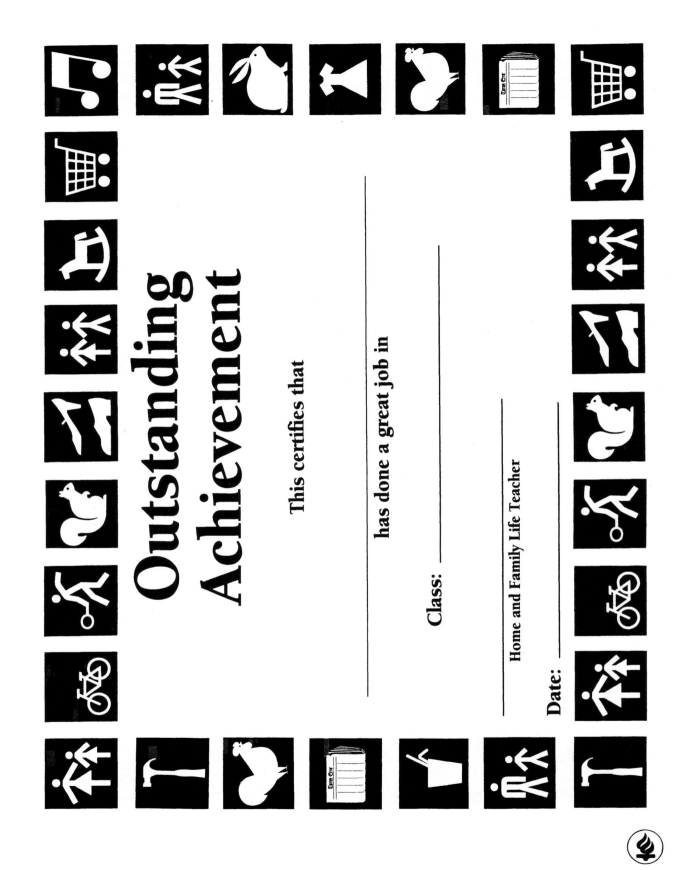

Outstanding Achievement

This certifies that

_____

has done a great job in

_____

Class: _____

_____
Home and Family Life Teacher

Date: _____

Home and Family Life Education

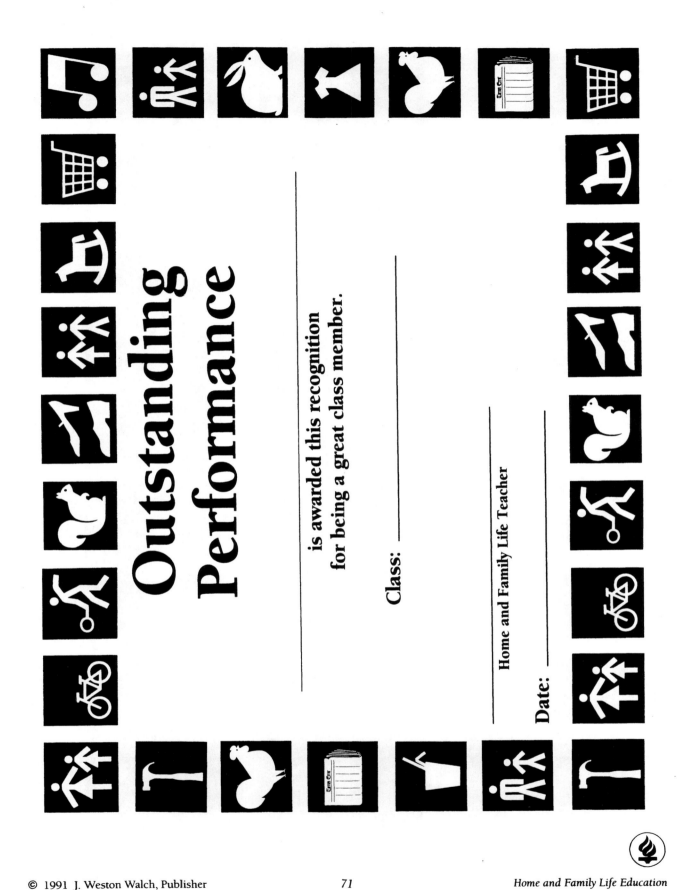

Outstanding Performance

is awarded this recognition
for being a great class member.

Class: _____

_____
Home and Family Life Teacher

Date: _____

Home and Family Life Education

Teamwork
Award

_____

**has been successful in being
a contributing member of the team.**

Class: _____

School: _____

_____
Home and Family Life Teacher

Date: _____

Rate This Class

Directions: Answer these questions carefully and honestly. You don't need to put your name on this paper. Your teacher is interested in your ideas for improving this class. If you need to elaborate on one of your answers, use the back of this paper.

Which class are you evaluating? _____

What grade do you expect to earn? _____

Did the class cover topics you were expecting to study?

yes _____   no _____

If not, what did you expect to study?

List the most interesting topics covered in this class.

List three things you liked best about this class.

1. _____

2. _____

3. _____

List three complaints or concerns you have about this class.

1. _____

2. _____

3. _____

List some suggestions you have for improving the concerns you note above.

Rate the following, by making a check in the appropriate column.

	Excellent	Good	Fair	Poor
Topics covered in class				
Class assignments				
Class activities				
Films, videos				
Speakers				

UNIT II

Food and Nutrition Activities

It's on the Label

Directions: Using the label provided in class, answer the following. If you cannot find a particular piece of information, leave that part blank.

Brand name

Generic or common name*

Net weight or contents*

Ingredients (underline those with which you are familiar)*

Manufacturer's name and address*

Dating code data (pull date)

Cost

UPC

On the back of this paper, summarize the directions for preparing your food product.

Nutritional Label (This is not required unless a product makes nutritional claims.)

Serving size* _____

Number of grams of the following per serving:*

carbohydrates _____

fats _____

proteins _____

Percentage of U.S. RDA (United States Recommended Daily Allowance) of the following:*

calcium _____

iron _____

vitamin A _____

vitamin C _____

thiamine _____

niacin _____

riboflavin _____

Other information on the nutritional label:

*This information is required by federal law.

Group members: _____ _____

_____ _____

Date: _____

Basic Four Game

Directions: Working in your team, circle the foods that belong in the Basic Four group called out by your teacher. When your team has circled all the correct foods in that group, take this paper to your teacher. The first team with all the correct answers wins!

milk	tacos	applesauce
oatmeal	deviled egg	bagels
strawberries	fruit yogurt	corn chips
cinnamon roll	blueberry muffin	root beer
orange juice	fruit punch	noodles
French toast	German chocolate cake	cheeseburger (with roll)
cantaloupe	cheese pizza	smoked salmon
croissants	roast turkey	barbecued spareribs
chocolate milk	corn on the cob	cherry Jell-O
scrambled eggs	mashed potatoes	chocolate pudding
eggnog	cranberry juice	potato salad
tomato juice	pasta salad	salami
watermelon	French fries	ripe olives
grapefruit	popcorn balls	peanut butter
walnuts	chocolate candy bar	cottage cheese
toast and jelly	cola	liver
whole wheat bread	peaches	baked apple
grape juice	strawberry shortcake	grits
baked beans	lemon-lime soda	chocolate ice cream
coffee (if sugared)	vanilla milkshake	banana split
pork chops	raspberries	hot buttered biscuit
omelet	shredded wheat with bananas	bran flakes
bacon	spaghetti and meatballs	soy sauce
ketchup	baked potato	iced tea (if sugared)

Home and Family Life Education

Name _____ Date _____

It's Snackin' Time

Directions: Cut out a picture of your favorite snack. Then, using the books in class, analyze your snack as to its nutrient content per serving.

A nutritional label for: _____

Serving size: _____

[in this area, glue a picture of your favorite snack]

One average serving of this snack has approximately _____ calories. An "average serving" is this size: _____ . My favorite snack belongs to the following Basic Four group(s): _____

Nutrient	Adult RDA	My Snack Amount	*or*	% RDA
Vitamin A	5000 IU	_____ IU		_____ %
Vitamin C	60 mg	_____ mg		_____ %
Niacin	20 mg	_____ mg		_____ %
Riboflavin	1.7 mg	_____ mg		_____ %
Thiamine	1.5 mg	_____ mg		_____ %
Calcium	1200 mg	_____ mg		_____ %
Iron	18 mg	_____ mg		_____ %

Home and Family Life Education

Nutrition Bingo
Playing Card

Directions: Important nutrients are listed below. Select 24 of the nutrients and write one in each square. Your teacher or a classmate will read a nutrition question; the answer will be one of these nutrients. If you know the answer and that nutrient is on your card, place a marker on that square. Call out "Nutrition!" when you have covered 5 squares down, across, or diagonally.

vitamin A	iron	minerals	Basic Four
vitamin C	magnesium	protein	bread & cereal group
vitamin D	calcium	fat	fruit & vegetable group
vitamin E	phosphorus	carbohydrates	milk/dairy group
vitamin K	iodine	calorie	meat/protein group
thiamine	zinc	water	fats, oils, sugars
niacin	potassium	nutrition	roughage
riboflavin	vitamins		

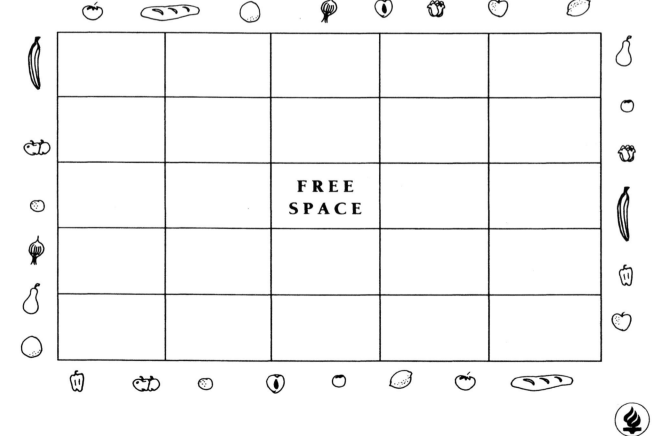

FREE
SPACE

Nutrition Bingo
Call Slips

This mineral is essential to the digestion of proteins, and it plays a part in the working of muscles and nerves.	**Magnesium**
Bagels, pita, doughnuts, and scones belong to this Basic Four group, an excellent source of carbohydrates.	**Bread & Cereal**
Sometimes called the fifth food group because the Basic Four provide no allowance for these; they give flavor to food.	**Fats, Oils, & Sugars**
This B vitamin prevents pellagra and is found in whole-grain breads, leafy green vegetables, and liver.	**Niacin**
This vitamin aids in the clotting of the blood and can be sold only by doctor's prescription because overdoses are fatal.	**Vitamin K**
Without this helper mineral, the body cannot use calcium.	**Phosphorus**

Name _____   Date _____

Nutrition Bingo
Call Slips

This vitamin is sometimes called the Complexion Vitamin and is found in dark green and deep yellow fruits and vegetables.	**Vitamin A**
This mineral is found in saltwater fish and iodized salt; it is necessary for a healthy thyroid gland and prevents a condition known as goiter.	**Iodine**
This mineral is necessary for maintaining the water balance in your body and for normal muscle action, including heart action.	**Potassium**
Humans need at least eight glasses of this a day and without it would die within a few days.	**Water**
The science of the food needs of the body.	**Nutrition**
This B vitamin is found in whole-grain breads, liver, and pork; it prevents a disease called beriberi.	**Thiamine**

Nutrition Bingo
Call Slips

This vitamin, the Sunshine Vitamin, is found in milk, cod liver oil, and egg yolk; it prevents a disease called rickets.	**Vitamin D**
Kumquats, zucchini, pomegranates, and avocados belong to this Basic Four group.	**Fruit & Vegetable**
If you carefully follow this daily food guide, you will have a balanced diet.	**Basic Four**
This B vitamin is necessary for healthy eyes and skin; the best sources are whole-grain breads, lean meats, and milk.	**Riboflavin**
The benefits of this vitamin are somewhat controversial, but it may slow the aging process, and it helps red blood cells function.	**Vitamin E**
These are special substances required for normal growth and nourishment of the body; they are found in milk, fresh fruits and vegetables, and whole-grain breads and cereals.	**Vitamins**

Nutrition Bingo
Call Slips

Besides vitamins, our bodies need these every day in very small quantities; examples are iron and calcium.	**Minerals**
Sometimes referred to as natural bulk or fiber; our bodies need this to keep them regulated.	**Roughage**
These carbon-oxygen compounds are necessary to give our bodies quick energy; they are found mainly in sugars and starches.	**Carbo-hydrates**
This substance is necessary for body fuel and warmth, gives flavor to food, and cushions the organs.	**Fat**
This substance is necessary for growth maintenance and repair of body tissue; it is found in meats, legumes, and milk.	**Protein**
Swiss cheese, cottage cheese, and ice cream would fit into this Basic Four group, which is an excellent source of calcium.	**Milk/Dairy**

Name _____   Date _____

Nutrition Bingo
Call Slips

A measurement of food energy.	**Calorie**
This vitamin is also called ascorbic acid; it helps keep cell walls strong, it may prevent colds, and it aids in healing.	**Vitamin C**
This mineral, found in milk products and leafy green vegetables, forms the basis for teeth and bones.	**Calcium**
This mineral is essential for the immediate digestion of carbohydrates, fat, and protein. It is also necessary for normal muscle function.	**Zinc**
Sausage, venison, beef, and eggs fit into this Basic Four group, which is an excellent source of protein and minerals.	**Meat/ Protein**
This mineral, found mostly in the blood, is essential for transporting and using oxygen throughout the body. A shortage of it leads to anemia.	**Iron**

Is It Safe to Cook?

Directions: Below, list ten kitchen safety rules and explain why these rules are important to follow.

Do's and Dont's	Explanation
1. _____ _____	_____ _____
2. _____ _____	_____ _____
3. _____ _____	_____ _____
4. _____ _____	_____ _____
5. _____ _____	_____ _____
6. _____ _____	_____ _____
7. _____ _____	_____ _____
8. _____ _____	_____ _____
9. _____ _____	_____ _____
10. _____ _____	_____ _____

Evaluate the rules listed by your group. Choose the ten best rules; then make a poster of these rules to display in your school kitchen.

Name _____   Date _____

_____

What's for Dinner?

What is your food to include? _____

_____

Using the cookbooks in class, find ten different ways to prepare the food. [This means boiled, baked, fried, etc., NOT ten different recipes for soup.]

Recipe name	Cookbook/page number	Preparation method
1.		
2.		
3.		
4.		
5.		
6.		
7.		
8.		
9.		
10.		

Home and Family Life Education

What's for Dinner? *(continued)*

Your recipes need to include:

BEEF STEW MEAT

Your recipes need to include:

PASTA

Your recipes need to include:

TURKEY

Your recipes need to include:

CHICKEN

Your recipes need to include:

TOMATO SAUCE or TOMATO PASTE

Your recipes need to include:

CABBAGE

Your recipes need to include:

CARROTS

Your recipes need to include:

GREEN BEANS

Your recipes need to include:

YOGURT

Your recipes need to include:

CHOPPED ONIONS

What's for Dinner? *(continued)*

Your recipes need to include:

POTATOES

Your recipes need to include:

PARMESAN CHEESE

Your recipes need to include:

CANNED TOMATOES

Your recipes need to include:

HAMBURGER

Your recipes need to include:

EGGS

Your recipes need to include:

RICE

Your recipes need to include:

NOODLES

Your recipes need to include:

MACARONI

Your recipes need to include:

COOKED CHICKEN

Your recipes need to include:

CELERY

Countdown to Dinner

Directions: When preparing a meal, one goal is to have all foods ready to serve at the same time. This requires careful planning.

Using a cookbook, select or plan a dinner menu for which you will prepare a time work plan. List your menu on this sheet and the time work plan on the second sheet of this assignment. Note: Your menu may include all or just parts of the menu plan listed below; the sample menu includes just parts of the menu plan.

Then find a recipe for the main dish of your dinner menu and use it to list (on the second sheet of this assigment) the food supplies and equipment you will need to prepare it.

Menu plan:	Sample menu:
Appetizer	(none)
Main Dish	Lasagna
Starchy Accompaniment	(none)
Salad	Tossed Green Salad
Vegetable	(none)
Bread	Garlic Bread
Beverage	Milk
Dessert	Chocolate Ice Cream

Recipe for the time work plan: _____

Cookbook used: _____ Page number: _____

Your dinner menu:

Countdown to Dinner
Planning Sheet

Food to prepare: _____

Food supplies needed:

_____   _____

_____   _____

_____   _____

_____   _____

_____   _____

Utensils/equipment needed:

_____   _____

_____   _____

_____   _____

_____   _____

_____   _____

Order of work for the entire meal   Time in minutes

1. _____   _____

2. _____   _____

3. _____   _____

4. _____   _____

5. _____   _____

6. _____   _____

7. _____   _____

8. _____   _____

9. _____   _____

Countdown to Dinner

SAMPLE MENU

Lasagna
Tossed Green Salad
Italian Dressing
Garlic Bread
Milk
Chocolate Ice Cream

Order of work for the entire meal	Time in minutes
1. _____	_____
2. _____	_____
3. _____	_____
4. _____	_____
5. _____	_____
6. _____	_____
7. _____	_____
8. _____	_____
9. _____	_____

Countdown to Dinner

Main Dish:

Lasagna

Food supplies needed:

_____   _____

_____   _____

_____   _____

_____   _____

_____   _____

Utensils/equipment needed:

_____   _____

_____   _____

_____   _____

_____   _____

_____   _____

UNIT III
Housing Activities

In My Opinion, a Home Should . . .

#1 Be able to tell the class your answer.
In my opinion, a home should be . . .

#2 Be able to tell the class your answer.
In my opinion, the most important fact in choosing a home is . . .

#3 Be able to tell the class your answer.
In my opinion, a good neighborhood is . . .

#4 Be able to tell the class your answer.
In my opinion, the greatest concern in setting up a new home would be . . .

#5 Be able to tell the class your answer.
In my opinion, privacy at home means . . .

#6 Be able to tell the class your answer.
In my opinion, the hardest thing about sharing living space is . . .

#7 Be able to tell the class your answer.
In my opinion, the hardest thing about creating the home I want would be . . .

In My Opinion, a Home Should . . . *(continued)*

#8   Be able to tell the class your answer.
In my opinion, the difference between a home and just a place to live is . . .

#9   Be able to tell the class your answer.
In my opinion, a home is a place to go when . . .

#10   Be able to tell the class your answer.
In my opinion, household insurance is important because . . .

#11   Be able to tell the class your answer.
In my opinion, I look forward to my own home because . . .

#12   Be able to tell the class your answer.
In my opinion, a beautiful home is . . .

#13   Be able to tell the class your answer.
In my opinion, a comfortable home is . . .

#14   Be able to tell the class your answer.
In my opinion, a convenient home is . . .

#15   Be able to tell the class your answer.
In my opinion, a good location for a home is . . .

In My Opinion, a Home Should . . . *(continued)*

#16 Be able to tell the class your answer.
In my opinion, good neighbors are . . .

#17 Be able to tell the class your answer.
In my opinion, a safe home is . . .

#18 Be able to tell the class your answer.
In my opinion, a home where I can bring my friends is . . .

#19 Be able to tell the class your answer.
In my opinion, the worst tragedy that could happen in a home is . . .

#20 Be able to tell the class your answer.
In my opinion, housing in the future will be . . .

#21 Be able to tell the class your answer.
In my opinion, three expenses associated with housing are . . .

#22 Be able to tell the class your answer.
In my opinion, the biggest problem in selecting a new home would be . . .

#23 Be able to tell the class your answer.
In my opinion, the main problem with living in an apartment is . . .

In My Opinion, a Home Should . . . *(continued)*

#24 Be able to tell the class your answer.
In my opinion, the best thing about living in a house is . . .

#25 Be able to tell the class your answer.
In my opinion, if my family was forced to move out of our home, I would feel . . .

#26 Be able to tell the class your answer.
In my opinion, the favorite room in my home is . . . because . . .

#27 Be able to tell the class your answer.
In my opinion, if my home disappeared today, I would feel . . .

#28 Be able to tell the class your answer.
In my opinion, if I could build a new home, I would . . .

#29 Be able to tell the class your answer.
In my opinion, if I could build my dream house, I would locate it . . .

#30 Be able to tell the class your answer.
In my opinion, the feeling or mood I would like to create in my home is . . .

Name _____ Date _____

The Inside Story of My Home (Houses)

Locate, describe, or *identify* the following for your own home. If you don't know the answer or do not have this in your home, leave the answer blank.

1. Tell how to get into:
   the attic _____

   _____

   the crawl space _____

   _____

2. Tell about your plumbing system:
   Where is the main water shutoff? _____

   _____

   Where are the local shutoffs (sink, toilet, etc.)? _____

   _____

   Where is the hot-water tank? _____

   _____

   Where is the septic tank or main sewer line? _____

   _____

3. Tell about the electrical system:
   Where is the fuse or circuit-breaker box? _____

   _____

   Where is the electric meter? _____

   _____

   What should you do if all the lights in one section of your home go out?

   _____

4. Tell about the heating system:
   What type do you have (gas, oil, electric, wood)? _____

   _____

   How do you completely turn off the heat? _____

   _____

101   *Home and Family Life Education*

The Inside Story of My Home (Apartments)

Locate, describe, or *identify* the following for your own home. If you don't know the answer or do not have this in your home, leave the answer blank.

1. Where can a person find out the rules of the apartment building?

   _____

2. How can a tenant contact the apartment management? _____

   _____

3. If you lose the key to your apartment, what is the procedure to follow?

   _____

4. What is the policy of your apartment manager to deal with tenant complaints? _____

5. Where would guests park their cars to visit you? _____

6. Tell about your plumbing system:

   Where are the local shutoffs (sink, toilet, etc.)? _____

   Where is the hot-water tank? _____

7. Tell about the electrical system:

   Where is the fuse or circuit-breaker box? _____

   What should you do if all the lights in one section of your apartment go

   out? _____

8. Tell about the heating system:

   What type do you have (gas, oil, electric, wood)? _____

   How do you completely turn off the heat? _____

9. What fire detection devices are used in your apartment complex?

   _____

   Where are they located? _____

10. What is available to ensure tenant security? _____

    Can the tenants install better locks? _____

   Home and Family Life Education

Group members: _____ _____

_____ _____

Date: _____

Safe, Not Sorry

Directions: In your group, discuss each question, then write the group's responses.

1. List five ways to make your home secure and safe for members of your family.

    a. _____

    b. _____

    c. _____

    d. _____

    e. _____

2. List five ways to "fool" a burglar into thinking that a family may be home, even if they are away.

    a. _____

    b. _____

    c. _____

    d. _____

    e. _____

3. What is the safest thing to do if you come home from school and find the main door open? You are usually the first one home. The door was locked when you left home that morning. _____

    _____

4. What is the best thing to do after a burglary has been committed? _____

    _____

5. How would you report a suspicious circumstance, person, or car in your neighborhood? _____

6. Tell how to make an emergency call. _____

    _____

Group members: _____   _____

_____   _____

Date: _____

Fire Safety Savvy

Directions: In your group, discuss the following, then write the answers.

1. List five ways to make your home fireproof:

    a. _____

    b. _____

    c. _____

    d. _____

    e. _____

    f. _____

2. General household fire safety:

    Where is it recommended that fire extinguishers be located? _____

    _____

    Where is it recommended that smoke detectors be located? _____

    _____

3. If the smoke detector goes off, tell how to evacuate your sleeping area.

    _____

    _____

4. Tell an alternate route if your first way is blocked by fire. _____

    _____

    _____

    What would you do if all your means of exit are blocked? _____

    _____

    _____

    On the back of this paper, draw the floor plan of your house or apartment. Then plan a family fire escape plan. Be sure to include two ways out of every room, as well as the family meeting place.

Group members: _____   _____

_____   _____

Date: _____

Focus on Safety

Directions: Use each letter as the beginning letter in a sentence of a safety rule. (Example: **H**—Have a fire extinguisher handy.)

H _____

O _____

M _____

E _____

S _____

A _____

F _____

E _____

T _____

Y _____

A _____

N _____

D _____

S _____

E _____

C _____

U _____

R _____

I _____

T _____

Y _____

Living Space Case Study Worksheet

1. Staple your case study here. Then answer the questions below. Put yourself in the position of the family in your case study.

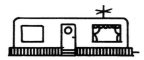

2. What are their housing needs?

   a. _____

   b. _____

   c. _____

   d. _____

3. In your opinion, which types of housing would be best?

   a. _____

   Why? _____

   b. _____

   Why? _____

   c. _____

   Why? _____

4. Find two want ads that describe appropriate housing for people in your
case study.

   a. _____

   Why? _____

   b. _____

   Why? _____

Living Space Case Studies

Family #1

Joe, age 38, and Sally, age 39, are married and have children. They both have jobs in a factory that manufactures parts for computers. Their combined yearly income is $42,000. They work opposite shifts—Sally works from 8 A.M. to 4 P.M., and Joe from 4 P.M. to midnight. This leaves at least one parent home to care for the children, ages 10 and 12. They spend their weekends doing things as a family—they especially like to hike in the mountains. They have a long-range goal of buying a home in the country with at least three acres.

Family #2

James, age 29, and Karen, age 28, have been married for six years. They don't have any children but are planning on starting a family next year. Karen is an attorney, earning about $39,000 a year. Jim works for his father and earns about $25,000 a year—he will take over his father's company when his father retires. Jim and Karen take two major vacations a year. They own a race horse and enjoy going to the track on race days. Karen is planning to return to school and work on an advanced degree within the next few months.

Family #3

Jack and Lili, ages 30 and 26, have been married for eight years. They have two children—Kim, age 7, and Sue, age 6. Lili is a housewife who likes to spend her spare time bowling. Jack works in an automotive repair shop. He makes $35,000 a year. Their main hobby is stock car racing.

Family #4

Karen, who is single, is 19 years old. She has recently moved out of her parents' home. She is a secretary and makes $18,000 a year. She has just finished paying off her car loan and now is looking for a good investment. She feels buying a home would be a good way to invest her money and have a place to live. Her hobbies include playing softball, going to parties, and occasionally doing some photographic modeling for extra money.

Living Space Case Studies *(continued)*

Family #5

Eileen is 20 years old. She is a typical college student who has to work her way through school. She makes about $5,600 a year through part-time work as a cashier in a discount store. She gets good grades, but she finds she must do a lot of studying, which leaves her little time for outside activities. Her hobbies include playing the flute, dancing, and gourmet cooking. She is thinking about moving into an apartment because her dormitory room is too far from her job and there is no convenient bus.

Family #6

Lila and Jim are both in their early 60's and plan on retiring in about two years. They feel they are lucky because they are both healthy—many of their friends have all kinds of ailments. They have two children, both married, and four grandchildren. Their combined yearly income is $60,000, and they are saving as much of that as they can for travel when they retire—they want to look up friends they have lost touch with over the years. They find that they don't need as much space in their home as they once did.

Family #7

Don and Marge Cromwell have three children, all adopted. Jim is 15 years old, Amy is 14, and Tom is 13. Tom is handicapped, as he was born with cerebral palsy. He is unable to walk up or down stairs, and he falls down a lot when he tries to walk without his crutches. Don earns $30,000 as a firefighter and works part-time selling encyclopedias—he earns $10,000 from this. Marge is a housewife and occasionally baby-sits in her home. The family is child-oriented and spends many evenings involved in the children's activities, such as sports or scouts.

Living Space Case Studies *(continued)*

Family #8

Four friends from high school decided to live together three years ago and are still together—they have learned to adapt to each other's quirks so they don't argue as much as they used to. Fran and Chris are both attending college and working part-time in a restaurant. They usually make about $500 a month each. Jennifer is employed as a dental assistant and earns about $18,000 a year. Amelia is a flight attendant—she has only been at that job for a month, so she isn't sure what she will be making, but she thinks about $25,000 a year to begin with. For leisure activities all four enjoy skiing, hiking, sunbathing, and gourmet cooking. They would like to live in a quiet, small town.

Family #9

Juan is 36 years old. He is married and lives with his wife, Rosa, and eight children. He is employed by a local trucking firm and is usually gone most of the week, as he specializes in long hauls. The family enjoys family-centered activities—especially family reunions, which sometimes last for a week! Juan's monthly income varies, but he can count on at least $2,500.

Family #10

Glenda is 28 years old. Right now she is single, but she has been married three times. She has three children—one from each marriage. Her children are 9, 6, and 3 years old. Her income as a night custodian is $18,000 a year. She is supposed to receive child support; so far she has been unable to collect, but she is working on receiving it. She should get $300 per month for each child. She lives close to her grandmother, who usually watches the children when Glenda is working.

Family #11

Otto is 62 and lonely! His wife died four years ago, and right now he lives with his dog, Henry, and his cat, Spot. Otto has eight grandchildren, who are very important to him. Usually at least one grandchild visits him every weekend. He is an expert piano tuner and earns $6,000 a year from that—he also gets Social Security and a pension from his lifetime career as a carpenter. From his retirement income, Otto gets about $750 a month.

Living Space Case Studies *(continued)*

Family #12
Charlie, age 25, and Arlene, age 26, have recently married, both for the second time. Charlie has child support payments to make to his ex-wife. Arlene must pay alimony for another year to her ex-husband, who cannot work due to an injury. Arlene is pregnant and due in about six months—this is their first child. Their combined income is $45,000 a year. Hobbies include yard work, sailing, and beachcombing.

Family #13
Betty, age 19, and Al, age 20, were married last month. They are both college students. Betty has two years left of college and Al has one. All of their income has gone to pay for schooling. This has created an unexpected burden on them. Their combined income is $15,000 a year. They have two huge loans out for college expenses, but these don't become due until after they graduate. Their interests are hiking, skiing, and seeing movies.

Family #14
Jason is 27 years old. He is single and lives with a roommate to meet expenses. He has almost finished his law degree and works in the public defender's office—his income is $2,800 a month from that job. His roommate runs a day-care center for needy families. Jason wants to marry his long-time girlfriend, Susanne, but cannot afford marriage in the near future. Jason likes to go to concerts and plays and do gourmet cooking.

Family #15
Richard, age 50, and Lynne, age 49, were recently married. Rich is a dentist making about $65,000 a year. Lynne is a social worker and makes about $22,000 a year. They entertain a lot and they also attend quite a few cultural events. Lynne also has a small counseling clinic out of their home—she specializes in victims of child abuse. They like to travel, especially to out-of-the-way places.

Home and Family Life Education

Living Space Case Studies *(continued)*

Family #16
Jack, age 20, and Jerry, age 21, are two college friends who room together. Their income is about $8,000 each—they both work in a gas station while going to school. They are both semiprofessional skiers—this requires a lot of physical training throughout the school year. Between school and skiing they have little time for anything else.

Family #17
This "family" consists of eight college men, ranging in age from 18 to 26. Their incomes vary, from $6,000 to $10,000 a year, including summer employment. Their interests are parties, dating, building race cars, rebuilding engines, and being rowdy. They all have loud stereos and jointly own a German shepherd named "Lucky."

Family #18
Terry and Barb, both 23, are newlyweds. Their combined incomes are $25,000 a year. Barb sells pottery at street fairs and Terry is a carpenter. They enjoy going to art museums and they like photography. Terry likes to do handy work around the house and he has a shop in the basement. Right now he is working on an oak dining room table for them.

Family #19
Ken and Diane have been married for five years. They don't have any children—in fact, they aren't planning to have any. Diane is a fashion coordinator for a large department store, and she makes about $30,000 a year plus overtime and bonuses. Ken is an electrician and makes $28,000 a year. They own their own acreage in the country, where they are beginning to start a tree nursery.

Family #20
Gordon, age 36, is single and likes the single life, preferring to date a variety of women. He is a medical doctor and makes $70,000 a year. He also has a lot of money invested in stocks, bonds, and real estate. He teaches classes to low-income families about health, nutrition, and personal care. He owns his own hunting equipment and likes to hunt in the mountains. He also owns a sailboat and a motor home—he entertains a lot using them.

Living Space Case Studies *(continued)*

Family #21

Emily is a widow who is 68 years old. She lives with her son, Bob. Her income is $1,200 a year from her husband's pension and $280 a month from Social Security. Her son's income is $45,000. She enjoys crocheting and playing cards at the local senior citizens' center. It is hard for Emily to live in her son's house, and she gets very crabby when things don't go her way.

Family #22

Dave, age 21, and JoAnne, age 20, are in college. They are in love and want to marry really soon. They know if they marry, their parents will stop paying their college expenses. Jo makes $6,000 a year from summer employment and part-time work during the school year. Dave makes $8,000 in his summer employment and part-time work as a security guard during the school year. They are both active in sports but spend a lot of time studying, even if they would rather be doing other things.

Family #23

Andy, age 45, and Harry, age 42, have been roommates since they were in college. They are both lawyers and lead very active bachelors' lives. Although they won't tell anyone their yearly income, it has to be at least $100,000 each. They like elegance in their home and they like to travel. They like to date many different women. They also spend a lot of time out of town working on various legal cases.

Family #24

Fred and Anne have two children. Fred is 36 years old. Anne is 34. Their children are Amy, who is 6, and Tim, age 10. Both of the children are very active in school and extracurricular activities with their friends. Fred earns $28,000 and Anne earns $34,000—they are both teachers. Anne and Fred travel a lot with their children. Fred also enjoys building racing cars—Anne has been known to drive one of the racing cars occasionally.

Family #25

Tracy is 53. She lives alone since being widowed over 20 years ago. She teaches chemistry at a high school where she also coaches tennis. Her annual income is $30,000. Her interests are painting, gardening, and traveling.

Living Space Case Studies *(continued)*

Family #26 — This family consists of four women; all work, and range in age from 22 to 28 years old. Their interests vary—writer, concert pianist, judo expert, and scuba diver. Incomes range from $18,000 to $30,000.

Family #27 — Robin and LeeAnn were married last fall. Robin is a mechanic at a lumberyard and makes about $25,000 a year. LeeAnn worked in a fast-food restaurant but has had to quit due to complications from an unexpected pregnancy. They can no longer live with her grandmother and must find a place of their own to live. Their interests are skydiving and attending rock concerts.

Family #28 — Marilyn and Bob were married last year. He brought two teenaged daughters to the marriage, and Marilyn has a 4-year-old son. They plan to have children of their own but not in the near future. Marilyn is a loan officer in a bank and Bob sells insurance. Their combined yearly income is about $45,000.

Family #29 — John could not wait to leave home, and three days after high school graduation he did. Now, four years later, he cannot afford an apartment, a car, and a dog on his salary and has moved home. His parents were looking forward to an "empty nest" but now have to consider John and his dog in their housing plans. They are charging John $125 a week for room and board.

Family #30 — Beverly and Scott have been married for over 20 years. Their two children are raised and have left home. Bev missed young children so much that she and Scott became foster parents and usually have two or three teenagers in their home for periods of time from one week to over a year. They must have a bedroom for each foster child.

Group members: _____   _____

_____   _____

Date: _____

This Is My Community

Directions: Answer the following questions for your community. If you don't know the answer or your community does not have the thing asked for, leave the answer blank.

1. Where is the closest:

   elementary school? _____

   public library? _____

   hospital? _____

   counseling service? _____

   police station? _____

   post office? _____

   public park? _____

   day-care center? _____

   employment office? _____

2. How would you obtain the following services?

   electricity _____

   gas _____

   cable TV _____

   telephone _____

   garbage collection _____

   water _____

3. Where can you go to:

   get your shoes repaired? _____

   get your TV repaired? _____

   get the immunizations necessary to go to school? _____

   register to vote? _____

   sign up for a community sports league such as Little League? _____

   mail a letter? _____

Group members: _____   _____

_____   _____

Date: _____

Design a Community of the Future

Directions: You are a group of community planners with vision! You have been given the task of planning for all the types of future communities listed below. However, you only have time to plan one before you are scheduled to present your ideas to a group of government officials. Choose one of the communities of the future listed below and sketch or graph the layout of the community.

Communities of the Future:

1. Space station

2. Self-contained underground community

3. Community under the ocean

4. Planned development of 150 acres

5. Planned urban condominium development

6. Isolated rural community

7. Future community described by your group

Your community must include a plan for meeting all the needs of people living in that community as they have been identified by your group. List the specific needs of your community below:

_____

_____

_____

_____

This project will be shared orally with the rest of the class. Your group will be evaluated on:

Creativity and uniqueness   Appearance of finished project

Completeness   Oral presentation

UNIT IV

Consumer Education Activities

Managing a Checking Account

Sally Shortskirts

Sally is popular and well liked at school. She is involved in a lot of activities and she is a careful money manager. Right now she has a savings goal of a trip to Mexico City. The beginning balance in her checking account was $184.08. She wrote a check to the Bridle Trails Horse Barn for $62.08 (board for her horse). Later that day she wrote a check to *Seventeen* magazine to renew her subscription ($18.00). On Saturday, Granny Goodsoul paid Sally for doing her housework ($15.00—Sally is embarrassed to charge her any more as Granny is on a limited pension). Sally deposited this money in her checking account. Sally decided that if she had any more income this month she would deposit it in her savings account (balance $689.12) so she would be closer to her savings goal. Checks cost Sally 15 cents each to write. The next day Sally went shopping with her best friend, Sylvia, at the mall. She needed a new pair of tennis shoes and found some on sale at the Bon Marché for $23.42; she paid by check. Another check went to Nordstrom's for $32.50 because she bought a warm-up suit so she could continue to participate in cross-country at school.

What is the balance in Sally's checking account?

Scratch Paper

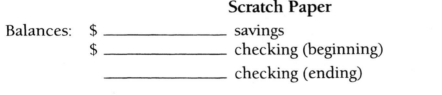

Balances: $ _____ savings
$ _____ checking (beginning)
_____ checking (ending)

List the four checks that need to be written:

_____ _____ $ _____ check fee _____
_____ _____ $ _____ "   "   _____
_____ _____ $ _____ "   "   _____
_____ _____ $ _____ "   "   _____

Write any deposits here, and tell whether to savings or checking:

$ _____ $ _____

Now finish the assignment by writing the checks and filling out any deposit slips that Sally may use.

Name _____ Date _____

Managing a Checking Account

Bruno Broadbottom

Bruno continually has money problems. Since last month, he has been able to build a small reserve in his checking account. As of last Monday, his checking account balance was $72.27, and he had $18.64 in savings. His first check was to the Magnificent Music Store for $22.75 for some new compact discs that he had wanted for a long time, and besides, they were on sale. Feeling so happy that he got such a good bargain, Bruno decided to buy a snack and wrote a check to Burgerville for $2.09! While he was sitting on the bench enjoying his snack, he remembered he was going to look at the jeans that were on sale at Nordstrom's. Bruno liked the style and fit and wrote a check out for $18.84 for one pair. Later that day Mrs. Neighbors finally paid Bruno $22.50 for baby-sitting, which he promptly deposited in his checking account. The next day Bruno purchased some books and a computer game at Payless for a total of $26.52. Bruno's bank does not charge him for checks because his parents have an account there.

What is the balance in Bruno's checking account?

Scratch Paper

Balances: $ _____ savings
            $ _____ checking (beginning)
            _____ checking (ending)

List the four checks that need to be written:

_____ _____ $ _____ check fee _____
_____ _____ $ _____ "   " _____
_____ _____ $ _____ "   " _____
_____ _____ $ _____ "   " _____

Write any deposits here, and tell whether to savings or checking:

$ _____ $ _____

Now finish the assignment by writing the checks and filling out any deposit slips that Bruno may use.

120   *Home and Family Life Education*

Managing a Checking Account

Sam Saddlesoap

Sam places a great value on thrift and savings. As of last Friday his savings account had a balance of $1,668.52. Last week he opened a checking account by depositing $200 he had received for his birthday. Yesterday he wrote a check for $12.58 for his monthly selection from the Science Fiction Book of the Month Club. His next check was to the Modern Music Store for $27.65 for two tapes of his favorite group. On the way home, Sam stopped at K Mart and bought a new video game for $31.90. After dinner Sam bought three blank videotapes at Payless for $18.02. Sam balanced his checking account and decided he was spending too much money (his brother teases him by calling him a miser). Today Sam went to the bank and closed his checking account. He decided that in the future he would pay for everything in cash!! It cost him 20 cents to write each check.

What is the balance in Sam's checking account?

Scratch Paper

Balances: $ _____ savings

$ _____ checking (beginning)

_____ checking (ending)

List the four checks that need to be written:

_____ _____ $ _____ check fee _____

_____ _____ $ _____ " " _____

_____ _____ $ _____ " " _____

_____ _____ $ _____ " " _____

Write any deposits here, and tell whether to savings or checking:

$ _____ $ _____

Now finish the assignment by writing the checks and filling out any deposit slips that Sam may use.

Name _____ Date _____

Managing a Checking Account

Laura Lostlove

Money is always a problem at Laura's home. Her father died three years ago, and her mother works as a waitress. There are six children at home. Laura baby-sits and does household chores to earn extra money. She has a regular Saturday job doing housework for the Friendly family. She has a savings goal to study to be an X-ray technician in a two-year course at a nearby community college. So far she has $197.42 in her savings account, and she hopes she won't have to withdraw it for a family emergency. Last week Laura's checking account had a balance of $84.22. Since then she has written these checks: Paul's Drug Store for lipstick and eye shadow—$8.22; Fashionable Fabrics for her school sewing project—$9.62; JC Penney for a birthday gift—$11.71; Johnny's Market for groceries—$12.51. Laura has the bad habit of not balancing her checkbook each time she writes a check. She thinks she may be overdrawn, so she deposits her baby-sitting check of $13.50 in her checking account. It costs Laura ten cents to write each check.

What is the balance in Laura's checking account?

Scratch Paper

Balances: $ _____ savings
            $ _____ checking (beginning)
            _____ checking (ending)

List the four checks that need to be written:

_____ _____ $ _____ check fee _____
_____ _____ $ _____   "   "   _____
_____ _____ $ _____   "   "   _____
_____ _____ $ _____   "   "   _____

Write any deposits here, and tell whether to savings or checking:

   $ _____ $ _____

Now finish the assignment by writing the checks and filling out any deposit slips that Laura may use.

Managing a Checking Account
Checks & Deposit Slip

CHECK NO. _____

_____ 19 ____ 71-587/749

PAY TO THE
ORDER OF _____ $ _____

_____ DOLLARS

MEMO _____ _____

074905872   251 372 8   4311

CHECK NO. _____

_____ 19 ____ 71-587/749

PAY TO THE
ORDER OF _____ $ _____

_____ DOLLARS

MEMO _____ _____

074905872   251 372 8   4311

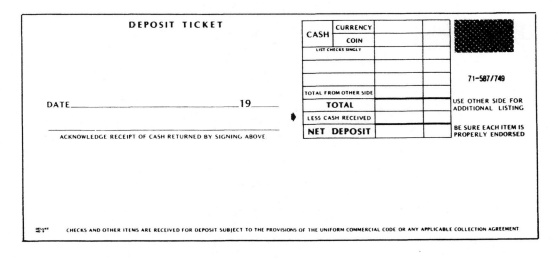

DEPOSIT TICKET

CASH	CURRENCY		
	COIN		
LIST CHECKS SINGLY			

71-587/749

DATE _____ 19 ____

TOTAL FROM OTHER SIDE		
TOTAL		
LESS CASH RECEIVED		
NET DEPOSIT		

USE OTHER SIDE FOR
ADDITIONAL LISTING

BE SURE EACH ITEM IS
PROPERLY ENDORSED

ACKNOWLEDGE RECEIPT OF CASH RETURNED BY SIGNING ABOVE

CHECKS AND OTHER ITEMS ARE RECEIVED FOR DEPOSIT SUBJECT TO THE PROVISIONS OF THE UNIFORM COMMERCIAL CODE OR ANY APPLICABLE COLLECTION AGREEMENT

Name _____ Date _____

Leroy Taylor's Checking Account

Last month Leroy Taylor wrote these checks and had the following deposits. His beginning balance was $1,846.83. It costs him 20 cents each time he writes a check.

#1010	Rainier View Apartments	(rent)	$460.00
#1011	Texaco	(gasoline)	$ 60.47
#1012	U.S. West Communications	(phone)	$ 29.83
#1013	Ford Motor Company	(car payment)	$314.16
	DEPOSIT		$802.99
#1014	Dr. Toothaker	(dental work)	$182.42
#1015	Puget Power	(electricity)	$204.99
	DEPOSIT		$ 21.47
#1016	United Airlines	(vacation!)	$ 99.00
#1017	The Bon Marché	(clothes)	$142.87
#1018	Nordstrom	(shoes)	$ 63.97
#1019	U.S. Bank	(traveler's checks)	$400.00

Use the information about Leroy's finances to fill in Leroy's checking account register below.

Number	Date	Check	Amt. of Check	Fee	Deposit	Balance	

Home and Family Life Education

Name _____ Date _____

Leroy Taylor's Vacation

Leroy Taylor just received his monthly bank statement. He is not sure how much money he has because he doesn't balance his checkbook every time he writes a check; he considers that "boring." He needs $650.00 to go on a vacation to Las Vegas.

Last month Leroy's beginning balance was $1,567.95. He wrote these checks and had these deposits:

#1021—Rainier View Apartments (rent), $460.00
#1022—Puget Power (electricity), $175.86
#1023—Chevron U.S.A. (gasoline), $162.90
#1024—Safeway (groceries), $60.00
     DEPOSIT $182.42
#1025—Albertson's (groceries), $45.00
#1026—Gene Juarez Hair Salon (haircut), $18.50

#1027—JC Penney (clothes), $68.83
#1028—Nordstrom's (vacation clothes), $142.35
     DEPOSIT $651.19
#1029—Dr. Anne Ginzberg (veterinarian), $42.50
#1030—Place Two (clothing), $192.41
#1031—American Express (credit card bill), $188.11
#1032—Frederick and Nelson (clothes), $104.50
#1033—Safeway (groceries), $85.00.

It costs Leroy 20 cents to write each check, and on the first of the month, he is charged a $5.00 monthly service fee.

Use the information about Leroy's finances to fill in Leroy's checking account register below. Look at Leroy's ending balance. Does he have enough to go on his vacation?

Number	Date	Check	Amt. of Check	Fee	Deposit	Balance	

Home and Family Life Education

Shopping Spree
Record Form

Charge to (Name) _____ Date _____

Quantity	Item	Cost/Unit	Total Amount of Purchase	Total Spent

Shopping Spree #1

Sunglasses $20

Home and Family Life Education

Gift for a Friend $15

Home and Family Life Education

Books, Magazines $10

133

Home and Family Life Education

Records, Tapes, and CDs $30

Home and Family Life Education

Miscellaneous Clothing $20

eston Walch, Publisher

Home and Family Life Education

A Quick Snack $5

Home and Family Life Education

Plants $15

Home and Family Life Education

Ticket to Concert or
Athletic Event $20

A New Pet $35

Home and Family Life Education

Pizza $5

147

Summer Clothes $45

149

Home and Family Life Education

Shoes $30

Home and Family Life Education

Winter Clothes $60

Home and Family Life Education

Day Spent on Recreation $30

155

Photography Equipment $65

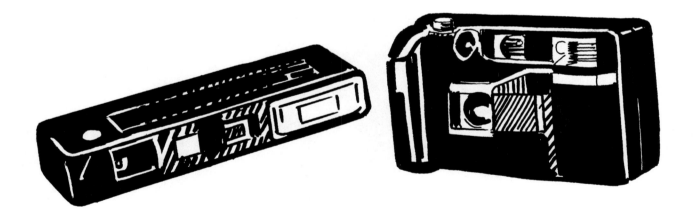

Home and Family Life Education

Camping or Outdoor Gear $25

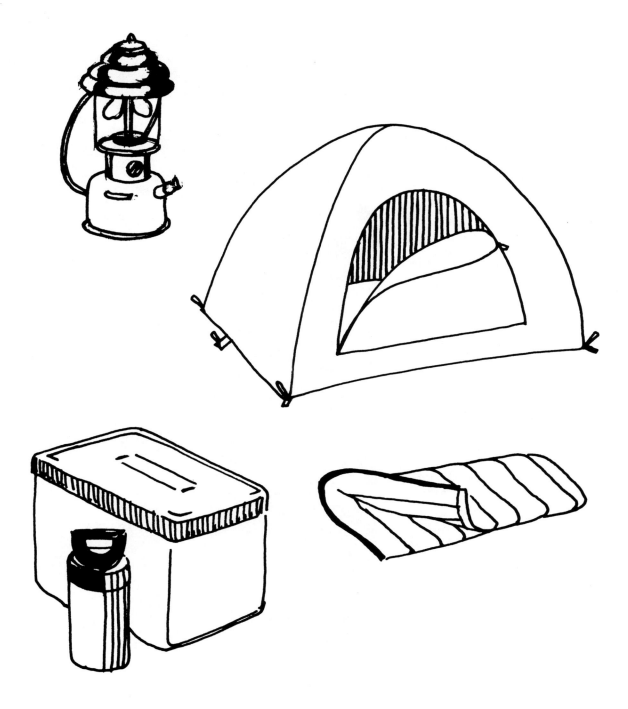

Designer Sheets $30

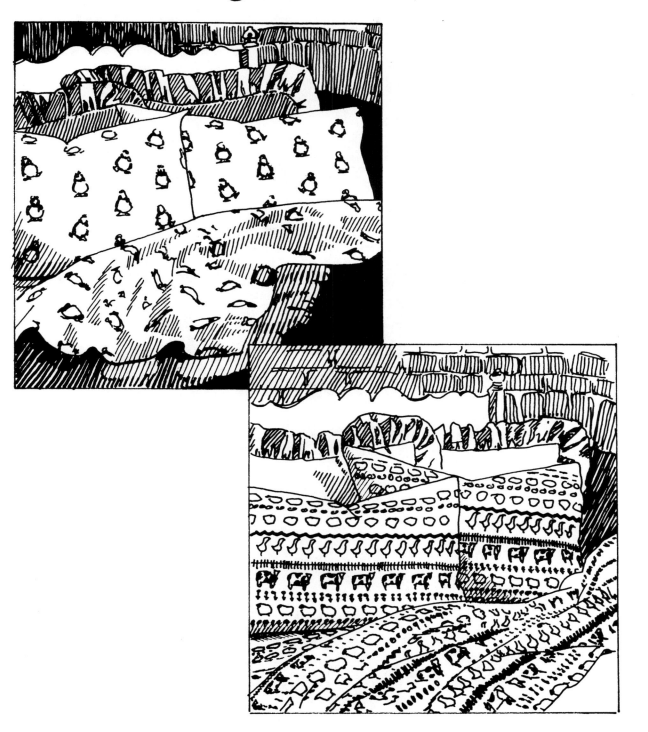

Home and Family Life Education

Warm Quilt or Blanket $65

Home and Family Life Education

A Phone $35

Shopping Spree #2

Tennis Shoes $40

Pass to Movie Theater $10

Home and Family Life Education

Materials for Hobby $20

AVIATION
25¢

Latest "Fad" $15

Home and Family Life Education

Sportswear $35

Home and Family Life Education

Fast Food Snack $5

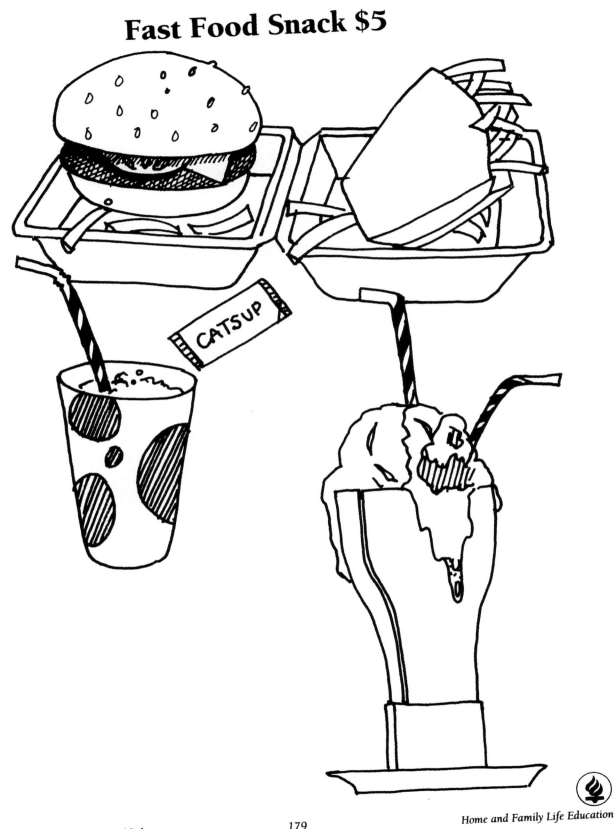

179

Computer Equipment
and Games $100

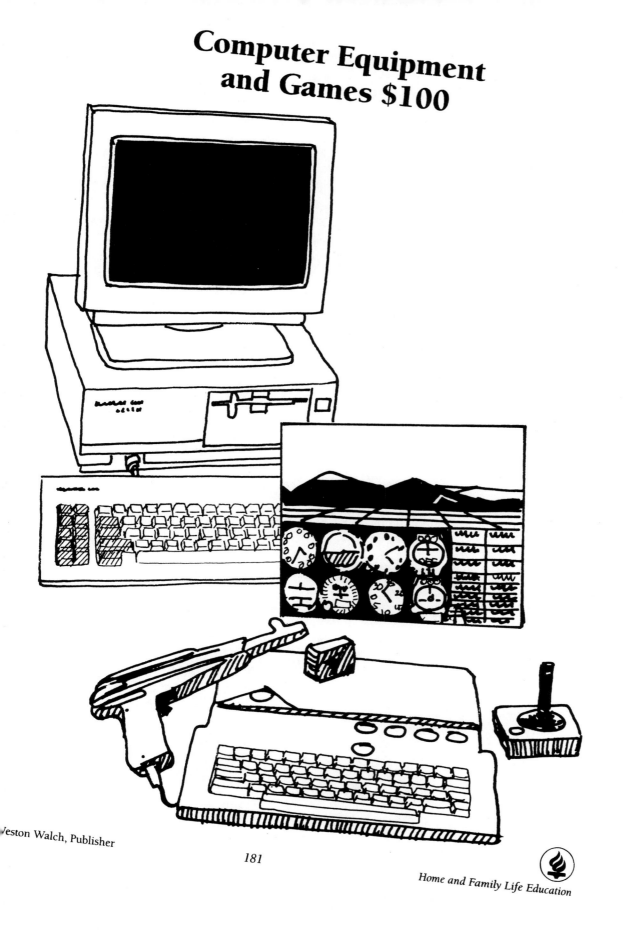

/eston Walch, Publisher

Home and Family Life Education

Portable "Sound" $35

Home and Family Life Education

Posters and Room Decorations $20

Athletic Clothing $25

Pants or Jeans $20

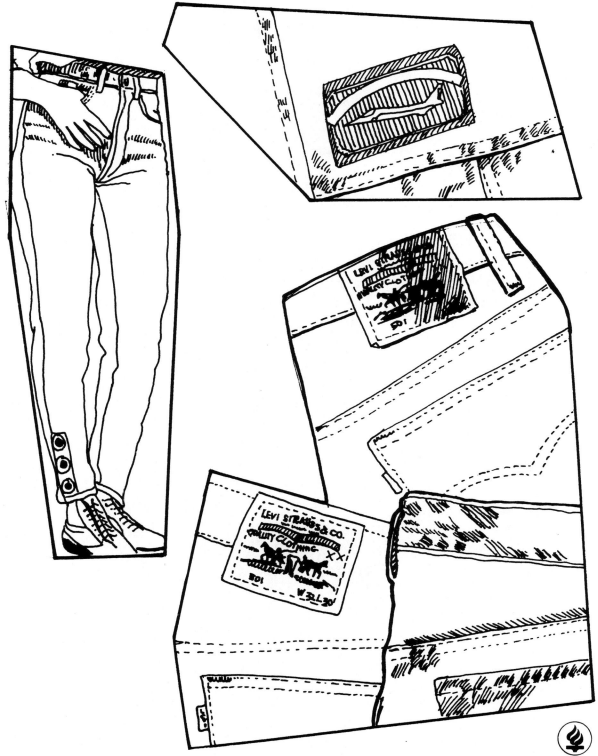

Home and Family Life Education

Gift for a Family Member $15

191

Season Pass to Recreation $50

FUN WORLD
Season Pass

Admit one for 1990 Fun World season . Good for all rides
Expires December 31, 1990

Home and Family Life Education

Athletic Equipment $35

Down Comforter $95

Home and Family Life Education

Small TV Set $100

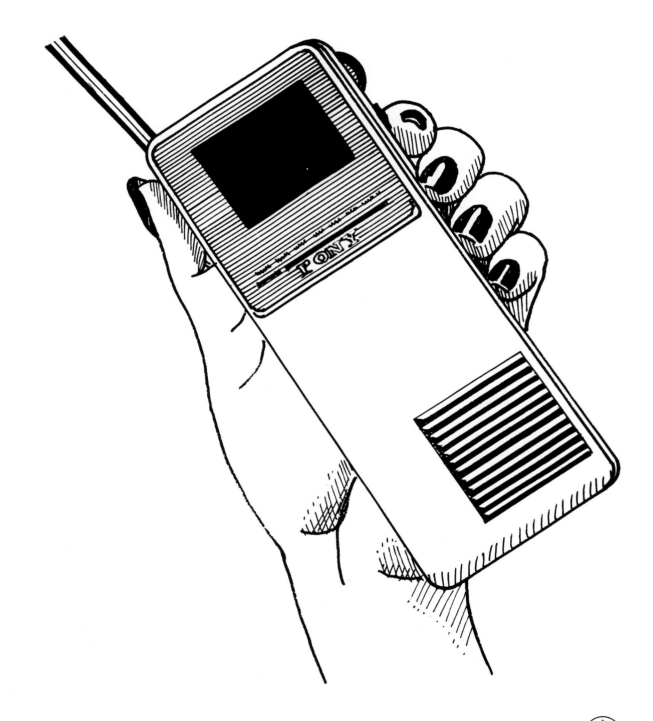

Home and Family Life Education

Jewelry $25

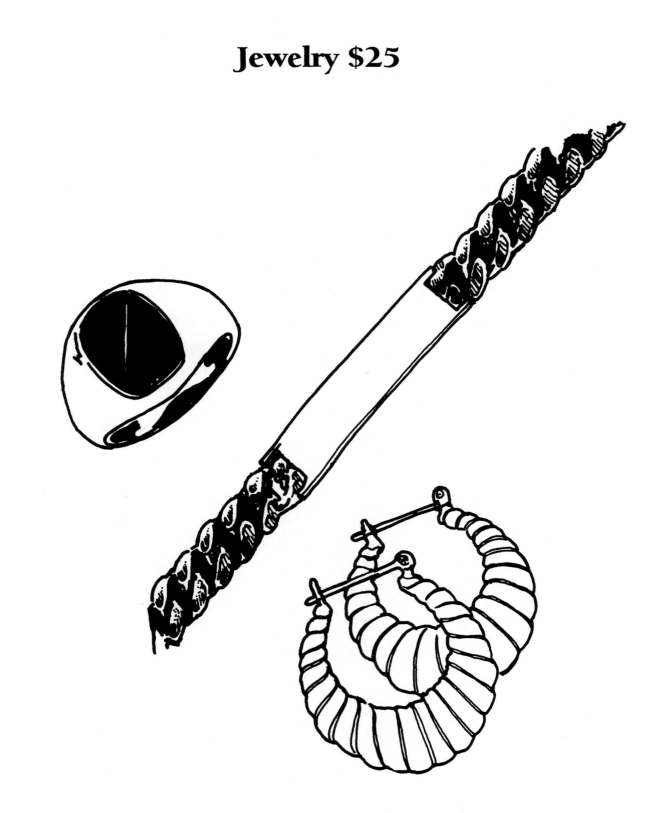

Home and Family Life Education

Hair Styling $30

Home and Family Life Education

Games $20

Consumerism from *A* to *Z*

Directions: Listed below are the letters of the alphabet. List as many consumerism vocabulary words as you can think of that begin with each letter of the alphabet. Include a short definition of each word.

A _____

B _____

C _____

D _____

E _____

F _____

G _____

H _____

I _____

J _____

K _____

L _____

M _____

N _____

O _____

P _____

Q _____

R _____

S _____

T _____

U _____

V _____

W _____

X _____

Y _____

Z _____

Group members: _____   _____

_____   _____

Date: _____

Where Does Family Income Go?—Phase One

Directions: Select a name for your "family." Then brainstorm what your group feels are this family's needs and wants. Based on your group's description of this family, list how they will spend their income.

Family name: _____

Describe the family members.

What are this family's needs?

What are this family's wants?

What is the family's gross monthly income? _____

This family will budget their monthly income as follows:

Amount	Item	Want or Need
$ _____	_____	_____
$ _____	_____	_____
$ _____	_____	_____
$ _____	_____	_____
$ _____	_____	_____
$ _____	_____	_____
$ _____	_____	_____
$ _____	_____	_____
$ _____	_____	_____
$ _____	_____	_____
$ _____	**Total spent**	

Group members: _____   _____

_____   _____

Date: _____

Where Does Family Income Go?—Phase Two

Directions: Now that you have planned the family's income, redo the budget by following what is considered "average" for a family. (For example: The figure for housing should be 27% of Total Disposable Income.)

$ _____   Gross Income

$ _____   Deductions for Social Security and Federal Income Tax

$ _____   Total Disposable Income

$ _____   Housing 27%

$ _____   Food 14%

$ _____   Transportation 19%

$ _____   Health Care 4%

$ _____   Clothing 5%

$ _____   Taxes 9%

$ _____   Other 22%
(insurance, pension, entertainment, etc.)
List what you would include for "other":

_____

_____

_____

Any savings? _____

How do these figures compare with the amounts you decided on for "Where Does Family Income Go?—Phase One"? How would you change the amounts on page 208 to be more in line with the figures on this page? Write your answers on the back of this sheet or on another piece of paper.

UNIT V
Relationships Activities

Group members: _____   _____

_____   _____

Date: _____

Safety First for Me

List personal safety tips for:

1. going to and from school

2. after-school activities

3. entering your home alone

4. friends in your home without adults present

5. answering the phone

6. answering the door

7. being home alone

8. being alone or with friends after dark

9. public places—bus stop, movie theater, shopping mall, park, rest rooms, etc.

How do you make an emergency call?

         Home and Family Life Education

What Do You Value?

Directions: Write your responses to the following. Your answers are personal, and there are no right or wrong answers.

1. Define personal values.

   _____

   _____

2. Where does a person get his or her own values?

   _____

   _____

3. Why do one person's values differ from the values of his or her closest friends?

   _____

   _____

4. What are some values that meet with society's approval?

   _____

   _____

5. Below, circle some values that you have:

friendship	honesty	family life
education	religion	privacy
the arts	popularity	recognition
independence	thrift	individuality
helpfulness	security	money
equal rights	self-improvement	new experiences
good health	patriotism	cleanliness
aesthetics	peace	freedom
care for the environment	creativity	appearance

Assignment: Cut out a "T-shirt" from a large piece of paper. Either draw or cut out pictures to put on the "T-shirt" that illustrate your five most important personal values. Do not put your name on the "T-shirt" because the class will try to guess whom the "T-shirt" belongs to.

Family Want Ads

Make a list of words that describe *positive* qualities you would like parents to have.

_____

Make a list of words that describe *positive* qualities you would like brothers and sisters to have.

_____

Make a list of words that describe *positive* qualities your family would hope teenagers would have.

_____

Want Ads are written to "sell" a product or job to a potential buyer. Keeping this in mind and using the word lists on page 214 as a beginning, write an ad to "sell" the following:

Perfect Parent: _____

_____

_____

Perfect Teenager: _____

_____

_____

Perfect Brother or Sister: _____

_____

_____

Yourself: _____

_____

_____

Share your ads with a group of classmates. Discuss how the ads are alike or different. As a team, select one ad from each category to share with the rest of the class.

Name ———————————————————————— Date ————————————

Family Portrait

Home and Family Life Education

Name _____ Date _____

Mapping Out the Rest of My Life

Directions: Each person is a part of everything that has happened before. Mark major events in your life on the following life line by drawing a line from that event to the year in which it happened. Next try to map out your future by projecting when other major events will occur, then drawing a line to the year you think each major event would happen. (Note: You do not need to use all events.)

first day of school	1975	own birth
	1980	
first job	1985	birth of siblings
high school graduation	1990	serious boyfriend/girlfriend
	1995	
leaving home	2000	becoming engaged
	2005	
first car	2010	getting married
first home	2015	first child is born
	2020	
moving to a new city	2025	second child is born
	2030	
changing jobs	2035	other children are born
deciding on life's career	2040	celebrate 40th birthday
	2045	
retirement	2050	first gray hair
	2055	
moving to smaller home		last child leaves home
	2060	
travel to another country	2065	death of husband/wife
	2070	
	2075	own death

Group members: _____   _____

_____   _____

Date: _____

Teen Rights and Responsibilities

Directions: Pretend you are the parents of teenagers whose task is to come to agreement on the basic requirements that should be met for a License for Teenagers.

A. Begin this task by brainstorming to produce a list of rights and responsibilities for teenagers.

Teen Rights	**Teen Responsibilities**
_____	_____
_____	_____
_____	_____
_____	_____
_____	_____
_____	_____

B. Now decide which teen right is most important. List it as #1 on the list below. Continue ranking the teen rights in order of importance until you have agreed on the top five teen rights. Follow the same procedure with the list of teen responsibilities.

Priority List

Teen Rights	**Teen Responsibilities**
1. _____	1. _____
2. _____	2. _____
3. _____	3. _____
4. _____	4. _____
5. _____	5. _____

Home and Family Life Education

License
for
Teenagers

After careful thought,
I have helped list the following
teen rights and responsibilities
and will try very hard to live up to them.

Teen Rights

_____

_____

_____

_____

_____

Teen Responsibilities

_____

_____

_____

_____

_____

_____

_____   _____
            Teenager   Parent(s)

Date _____

Clothing
Activities

Group members: _____ _____

_____ _____

Date: _____

Super Shopper

Directions: It is a good idea for a consumer carefully to check over an article of clothing before purchasing it. Below are specific details a careful consumer checks before purchasing clothing. In your group, discuss the importance of each of these and write your responses.

style _____

_____

fabric _____

_____

care label _____

_____

seams _____

_____

hems _____

_____

sleeves _____

_____

collar _____

_____

trim _____

_____

zippers/closures _____

_____

buttons/buttonholes _____

_____

fit _____

_____

Headless People

Home and Family Life Education

Headless People

Home and Family Life Education

Women's Faces

Home and Family Life Education

Men's Faces

Name _____   Date _____

_____

Where Can I Shop for Clothing?

Directions: Below are listed some types of retail stores that sell clothing. List the advantages and disadvantages of shopping in each type of store.

	Advantages	Disadvantages
Thrift store		
Consignment shop		
Factory outlet		
Chain store		
Specialty shop		
Department store		
Discount store		
Shopping mall		
Mail order		
"Party time"		

Your Clothing Costs

Directions:

1. Estimate the cost of the clothing you are wearing right now (this would be everything you take off to take a shower, so braces would not be included, but eyeglasses would).

shirt/blouse/sweater	$	_____
pants/skirt/dress	$	_____
underwear	$	_____
shoes/socks	$	_____
jewelry, etc.	$	_____
miscellaneous	$	_____
total	$	_____

2. Next, multiply this by the number of people in your family:

   $ _____ × _____ people = $ _____

3. What does it cost your family to clothe each person for a day?

Summary questions:

1. What made you decide to wear what you have on today?

2. What implications does this have for the family budget?

3. If, for some reason, you had only half as much money to spend on clothes, what changes would you make?

4. If you had double the amount of money for clothes, what would you do?

5. What did you do with the clothes you wore yesterday? (Hang them up, put them aside to be laundered, or leave them in a pile on the floor?)

Home and Family Life Education

What Would I Wear When . . . ?

Directions: Choose four of the following. Cut out pictures from magazines or newspapers to illustrate each one. Then tell WHY you chose each outfit.

Job interview

Formal dance

Concert

Evening school concert or play

School clothes shopping

Wedding

Professional sports event (soccer, baseball, etc.)

School baseball or football game

School field trip

Dinner at an expensive restaurant

After-school basketball turnout

Picnic

Speech at school assembly

Winter sports carnival

Family reunion

Birthday party at friend's house

Home and Family Life Education

UNIT VII
Child Development Activities

Group members: _____ _____

Date: _____

Baby-sitting Basics

Directions: Answer the questions about what a responsible baby-sitter would do.

1. The main reason parents hire baby-sitters is . . .

_____

_____

2. It is important for a baby-sitter to know something about the family before sitting for them because . . .

_____

_____

3. A good baby-sitter arrives early for the job because . . .

_____

_____

4. The amount you are to be paid should be discussed **before** baby-sitting because . . .

_____

_____

5. A baby-sitter needs to write down the parents' instructions before they leave because . . .

_____

_____

6. The baby-sitter needs to ask for a tour of the house because . . .

_____

_____

(continued)

Group members: _____ _____

_____ _____

Date: _____

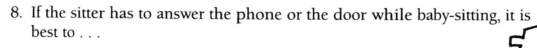

Baby-sitting Basics (*continued*)

7. It is best for a baby-sitter not to have friends over or call friends during baby-sitting because . . .

_____

8. If the sitter has to answer the phone or the door while baby-sitting, it is best to . . .

_____

9. The best way to keep the children safe while baby-sitting is for the sitter to . . .

_____

10. The first rule in an emergency is to . . .

_____

11. In case of an emergency, the first people to be notified are . . .

_____

12. Some easy and nutritious snacks that a baby-sitter could prepare for children are . . .

_____

13. Some ways to entertain a preschooler are . . .

_____

14. Special care an infant needs is . . .

_____

15. Just before the parents are due home, some things the baby-sitter should do are . . .

_____

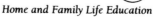

Home and Family Life Education

Baby-sitting Dilemmas

 # 1 Megan, age 4, does not want her parents to leave her at home. She wants to go too. She has a temper tantrum as her parents go out the door.

 # 2 Mr. and Mrs. Taylor ask the baby-sitter to wash all the dishes and clean the kitchen. It is obvious that the dishes have not been washed for some time. The Taylors mention this just as they are leaving. Their children are ages 3, 4, and 7 years.

 # 3 Chris is baby-sitting for the Abbot children. He asks a friend to come over and "help." While there the friend suggests that they go through the Abbots' CDs and use their new compact disc player.

 # 4 It is bedtime for Mark, age 7, and Mike, age 6. They tell the baby-sitter that every night they get a glass of soda and a candy bar before they go to bed. They then say that they cannot go to sleep unless they have them.

 # 5 The Andrews children are fighting again. This is the tenth time since their parents left three hours ago.

 # 6 The baby-sitter has a regular job baby-sitting for the Burtons every evening from 6 until 8 P.M. The caller on the phone insists on speaking to Mr. Burton.

 # 7 When the Greens return home, it is very apparent that they both have had too much to drink. Mrs. Green insists on driving the baby-sitter home.

 # 8 The big chocolate cake looks delicious, and there are other good things to eat in the refrigerator. The baby-sitter is very hungry. Mrs. Wright did not tell the baby-sitter to "help yourself" to the food, but she also didn't say not to eat anything.

Baby-sitting Dilemmas *(continued)*

#9   The baby-sitter wants more baby-sitting jobs to earn money to buy some gifts and to spend on next summer's vacation.

#10   Mr. Malone calls to ask if Sam can baby-sit Saturday night. Sam does not know the Malones, nor is he sure he knows where they live. Sam wants the money.

#11   The baby-sitter put 4-year-old Gary to bed at 7:00, but Gary has gotten out of bed six times since then.

#12   The baby-sitter has been at the Sterns' house since 7 P.M. It is now 10:30 P.M. and the doorbell rings. The Sterns are expected home at midnight.

#13   When Sally figures out what Mrs. Russell owes her for baby-sitting, it is $8.00, but Mrs. Russell only offers her $6.00.

#14   Everyone is in bed, asleep. The baby-sitter is doing homework and he thinks he smells smoke. Is the house on fire?

#15   The baby-sitter has never baby-sat 5-month-old Erin before. Erin has not stopped crying since her parents left.

#16   Five-year-old Bradley tells the baby-sitter that he will tell his parents never to have the baby-sitter back unless the baby-sitter promises not to tell his parents that he got into their private closet, which is off-limits for Bradley.

#17   Sara, age 5, just stands and stares at the baby-sitter as if she is very afraid.

Baby-sitting Dilemmas *(continued)*

#18 The Olsens have hired a baby-sitter for all day Saturday. When the sitter arrives, it is pouring rain! The children have to stay in the house all day—they are ages 4 and 7.

#19 Amy misses her parents, and she insists on calling them at the party they are attending. The baby-sitter is tired of listening to her tell how lonely she is.

#20 The Bergs have left strict orders that Eddie is to be in bed by 8:00 P.M. It is 7:58, and Eddie is refusing to get ready for bed.

#21 Cindy tells the baby-sitter that it is perfectly fine with Cindy's parents for her to empty the bookcase, the linen closet, and the desk drawers. She proceeds to do so. The baby-sitter doesn't know what to do.

#22 The baby-sitter has not seen Allen for 10 minutes. Earlier he threatened to run away because his parents didn't take him with them when they left. Allen is 7.

#23 The baby-sitter goes into Greg's room to check on him. The sitter discovers that Greg has wet the bed. Greg is 8 years old.

#24 It is 11 P.M. Someone is knocking on the window. The baby-sitter thinks it is some friends who are trying to scare her. She doesn't want to look outside because she doesn't want them to think she is afraid.

#25 Bill, who is 7, has been playing on the floor with his marbles. Dennis, who is 18 months old, just woke up from his nap and has started playing with the marbles.

Baby-sitting Dilemmas *(continued)*

#26 The baby-sitter is busy fixing lunch for two children. In the middle of the lunch preparation, 2-year old Jackie comes into the kitchen carrying an empty bottle of aspirin.

#27 Jennifer's mother told the baby-sitter to put Jennifer to bed by 9 P.M. Jennifer told the baby-sitter that her mother lets her stay up late on Saturday nights and watch TV. Jennifer, age 9, says her mother must have forgotten what night it is.

#28 Melissa burnt herself on the toaster. She is loudly crying and keeps asking for her daddy. The burn doesn't look too serious, but the baby-sitter has never taken a first-aid class.

#29 Paul was outside riding his bike. The baby-sitter was inside watching TV. Paul lost control of his bike on some loose gravel and skinned his knee. It looks awful.

#30 The baby-sitter is baby-sitting for the Snyders. Suddenly she notices smoke coming out of the back of the house next door.

#31 Both children are crying loudly because the dog has gone outside and hasn't come in. It is after dark, and the dog won't come when the baby-sitter calls.

Baby-sitting Dilemmas
Worksheet

Directions: Staple the dilemma you selected below, then answer the questions.

1. In your own words, what is the problem?

   _____

   _____

2. What are three ways to handle this problem?

   a. _____

   _____

   b. _____

   _____

   c. _____

   _____

3. Which one did you choose?

   _____

   Why? _____

   _____

   _____

4. What happened next in the story?

   _____

   _____

Design a Child

Home and Family Life Education

Group members: _____ _____

_____ _____

Date: _____

As Children Grow, They Change

Directions: Circle the developmental age for which you will be doing research. After you have completed the research, make a poster to share this information with the rest of the class. Use the resource materials in class and in the school library.

newborn   active 4's
busy babies   fascinating 5's
terrible 2's   school age
sweet 3's

Physical development

_____

_____

Intellectual development

_____

_____

Social development

_____

_____

Special tips for baby-sitters

_____

_____

Ways to entertain this age group

_____

_____

Special safety concerns

_____

_____

Children's Work Is Play!

Directions: Develop a game, a story, or a toy for a preschooler that a baby-sitter could take along when sitting for a child.

Guidelines for these projects

If you select a game—
It should:
encourage fairness
be fun
actively involve the child
have easy rules
allow each child to feel special

If you select a story—
It should:
hold the child's interest
be age-appropriate
be colorfully illustrated
be fun for the child
have characters the child can relate to

If you select a toy—
It should be:
attractive
safe and durable
fun
age-appropriate
able to contribute to physical, intellectual, and social
development
able to hold the child's interest